HOW TO IDENTIFY PLANTS

Also by H. D. Harrington
Manual of the Plants of Colorado

HOW

TO IDENTIFY

PLANTS

by

H. D. HARRINGTON

Professor of Botany and Curator of the Herbarium
Colorado State University

Illustrated by L. W. Durrell

Emeritus Professor of Botany
Colorado State University

SWALLOW PRESS
ATHENS, OHIO • CHICAGO

Swallow Press Books
are published by
Ohio University Press
Athens, Ohio 45701

Reprinted in 1979 by Ohio University Press
Second Ohio University Press Printing 1981
Third printing by Ohio University Press 1986

ISBN 0-8040-0149-9
LIBRARY OF CONGRESS CATALOG CARD NUMBER 57-4731

TABLE OF CONTENTS

PREFACE

The purpose of this book is to provide practical help for those interested in learning the special technique of identifying plants. It is based on the writer's experience in watching several thousand beginners acquire this skill. Unfortunately there is no easy way, no "royal road" to this knowledge. Like everything else worth while in life it takes effort and perseverance. An attempt is made here to smooth out some of the rough places on the road but the real job must be done by the student himself.

The procedure followed in dealing with the necessary technical terms is to present the common ones in a special chapter where related concepts can be compared with each other. It is suggested that these terms be memorized by the student. The more unusual ones can be looked up as needed in the illustrated glossary that makes up the final chapter. The definitions of many of these terms have been deliberately simplified in order to give a practical instead of a theoretical treatment. The real test in drawing up these definitions was how the term was used in the average manual for the identification of plants. The illustrations are intended to present the general concept and therefore are not drawn from actual specimens. A picture is a static thing but the concept it represents may be a variable one. Sometimes a series of drawings is used to represent this range of variation - when only one is given it shows an average. The specimen will rarely if ever look exactly like the drawing but must conform to the general concept of the descriptive term as illustrated by it.

Chapter I

INTRODUCTION

WHY WE NEED TO IDENTIFY PLANTS.

Many people are interested in learning the
names of the plants growing about them. The motives
behind this desire are probably many but it may be
of interest to list some of the commonest ones as expressed to the writer.

1. To satisfy a general curiosity.

Usually the first question that comes to mind
when one is confronted with a new and strange object
is, "Now what is the name of that?"

2. To be able to talk or write about the plant.

When an object must be designated again and
again then some sort of name for it becomes a real
need. As one person expressed it to the writer,
"Why, even a wrong name is better than no name at
all!" It might be possible to talk about plants or
keep written records concerning them, if each was
designated by an arbitrary number, but the procedure
would certainly be both tedious and unsatisfying.

3. To be able to look up information about the plant.

The great storehouse of human knowledge contains recorded facts concerning many species of
plants. Questions may arise like the following. Is
the plant edible? Is it poisonous to man or to his
livestock? How palatable is it to animals? Does
it have a tendency to become a weed and if so how can
it be controlled? How should it be treated in cultivation? Does it have any special legend or interesting story connected with it?

These questions and many others may be answered
very completely in various publications. However,
all this information is ordinarily unavailable to the
student if the name of the plant is unknown. If the
first question is "What is the name of that?" then

1

the second often is, "What good is it; what is it used for?" Knowing the name of a plant opens the door to the answer to such a question.

HOW NAMES OF PLANTS CAN BE LEARNED.

The names of plants can be learned in at least two ways.

1. Ask someone who knows.

This method is satisfactory when dealing with rather few numbers and when your authority is constantly at hand. Probably this is the most enjoyable way of learning the names of plants, as a boy who becomes acquainted with trees by having them pointed out by his father. However, few of us have this opportunity of constant expert advice. Add to this the fact that our trusted authority may turn out to be a broken reed and we may learn a lot of incorrect names! It is just as hard to learn the wrong names as the right ones. The sad fact seems to be that the less some people know about plants the surer they are in making snap identifications! A real expert is always cautious, sometimes exasperatingly so!

2. Learn to identify the plants yourself.

This is the best and surest way because you can determine plants anywhere and at any time. All that is necessary is the correct manual or flora and the skill to use it. As indicated in the preface this skill is not easy to acquire. The writer periodically receives a desperate request, "Please tell me an easy method of learning to identify plants." There just isn't any such thing. Popular treatments and picture books of plants may be satisfactory if all that is wanted is a superficial viewpoint but they can never lead to a real fundamental knowledge of the subject.

WHY PLANT IDENTIFICATION CANNOT BE MADE EASY.

1. There is a special knack involved.

Some people pick up this skill more quickly than others. Discouragement always comes at the beginning when progress seems slow.

2. Technical descriptive terms must be mastered.

These terms are freely used by the manuals because they have a definite and exact meaning that
cannot be expressed in ordinary language, at least
with reasonable brevity. For example, two related
species may differ only in the type of hairs on the
leaf surface, one "tomentose", the other "pilose".
This is a clear cut difference to one who understands
these terms but almost impossible to state briefly in
anything but botanical parlance. At least three ways
of mastering these technical terms are possible.

(1.) Deal with each new term as it is encoun-
tered. Almost every manual includes a
glossary explaining these terms.

(2.) Attempt to memorize all or most of the
terms used by the manual and try to understand their exact meaning before starting
the identification proper.

(3.) Drill on the important terms that are con-
tinually used and look up the others as
needed.

The writer believes that the third method is the
best for students. The first one slows the work down
so much that a beginner becomes discouraged. The
second method would surely work out but it would certainly be monotonous and uninteresting. The last procedure allows one to understand these commonly used
terms better by giving a chance to compare related
ones. For example the exact meaning of "lanceolate"
as a leaf shape (Fig. 107) becomes apparent when one
compares it with the related "linear" (Fig. 106) and
"ovate" (Fig. 108). This third plan is the one on
which this booklet is based. The next eight chapters
are given over to a discussion of the terms that have
been found to be most important. It is suggested
that the student becomes so familiar with them that
they need not be looked up each time they are used.
An illustrated glossary is presented as the last
chapter to aid in the understanding of the less commonly used terms.

Some students find it worth while to keep a list
of each new term with its definition. These can be
reviewed from time to time. However, some of the

names on this list may be uncommon and may not be
used again for some time. Form the habit of checking the meaning of each new term as it comes up.
Trying to get the meaning from the context, comparing
it with its contrasting term, skipping over the
phrase and trusting to luck - all these methods may
work in certain cases but can never lead to a real
skill in identifying plants.

3. Constant practice is necessary.

       This means that a student must be really in
earnest about acquiring the skill. Either a stern
necessity or an unflagging determination (or both)
are prerequisites in learning to identify plants.

       The most efficient method of acquiring this
technique is to learn it under the direction of some
competent teacher where help can be given when it is
most needed. However, many people in various walks
of life have picked up this discipline entirely on
their own without the aid of a formal course in the
subject. Some of them have even become world wide
authorities on special plant groups or on the flora
of a limited area. A few have even wound up as
teachers of the subject. Remember, do not allow
yourself to become discouraged at first. Acquiring
a skill or any special knowledge is much like rolling
up a snowball - it appears to grow so slowly at first
but enlarges with satisfying rapidity when it begins
to attain a large diameter.

NECESSARY EQUIPMENT.

1. The manual or flora covering the area.

       These will be discussed in a later chapter.

2. Hand lens.

       A good lens is a necessity, probably something
between an 8 X (8 times magnification) and a 12 X.
The lower powered ones are larger and give a bigger
field with a longer working distance. The higher
powered ones are smaller and therefore easier to
carry but although the image is magnified more it is
not so clear. A good lens has a reasonably long
working distance and gives a reasonably clear image
even out toward the edge of the field. A common type
of hand lens is shown in Fig. 1 A.

Fig. 1.

3. Forceps and needles.

These implements allow for the handling of minute parts. The forceps are shown in Fig. 1 D., a needle in Fig. 1 E.

4. Razor blade.

A sharp blade is needed in order to make thin sections of flower ovaries. An ordinary knife blade is not satisfactory even when very sharp. A straight edge razor works nicely if kept keen-edged. Most students prefer to purchase a package of one-edge safety razor blades, discarding the dull ones from time to time. A holder for razor blades is on the market and may prove to be a convenience. Such a razor knife is shown in Fig. 1 C.

The blade should be used with a pulling or pushing diagonal motion, not a chopping action but more on the order of manipulating a saw than an axe. This is illustrated in Fig. 39 in Chapter IV.

5. Rule.

Be sure the rule is graduated in centimeters and millimeters; practically all manuals and floras give

measurements according to the metric system. Such a
rule is shown in Fig. 1 B.

Chapter II

HOW PLANTS ARE CLASSIFIED

Before the technique of identifying plants is developed the student should have in mind the way plants are grouped together and how these various groups are organized. It is often amazing for a beginner to observe how strikingly plants can be segregated into various divisions and subdivisions. For example, species of the genus Rosa the world over have an unmistakable stamp of the "rose" upon them. Man has attempted to recognize and name these natural groupings. It is true that intergradations do exist in some groups with exasperating regularity. We are apt to notice these exceptions as we would one obstreperous child among a group of well behaved ones and forget the fact that the great majority of plants actually seem to group themselves naturally into large and small units.

NEED FOR CLASSIFYING.

Several hundred thousand species of plants exist in the world. A recent estimate placed the number at 335,000. The single state of Arizona was listed by Kearney and Peebles in their Arizona Flora as having 132 families, 907 genera and 3,370 species. So even the flora of one state poses a definite problem in organization; somehow we must get the plants pigeonholed. In a herbarium it is necessary to file the specimens away according to some system. We could file them away in some artificial arrangement - as for example trees, shrubs and herbaceous plants - or we could arrange them alphabetically by name. Botanists have chosen to try to organize, classify and group plants according to what they think has been their evolutionary development, that is, in a phylogenetic system with related plants contiguous and unrelated plants far apart.

A TYPICAL SYSTEM.

Species - the plants of one kind.
Genus - a group of related species.
Family - a group of related genera.

Order - a group of related families.
Class - a group of related orders.
Subdivision - a group of related classes.
Division - a group of related subdivisions.

The four divisions of the plant kingdom as outlined in many manuals and books on general botany
are:

1. Thallophyta (Thallophytes). The algae and
   fungi.
2. Bryophyta (Bryophytes). The mosses and
   liverworts.
3. Pteridophyta (Pteridophytes). The ferns and
   fern allies.
4. Spermatophyta (Spermatophytes). The seed
   plants.

The four groups are sometimes called phyla instead of divisions and some authors may not organize
them into categories of equal rank. You will want to
become familiar with the way your manual outlines
these major groups. Most ordinary books for the i-
dentification of plants include only the last two,
the so-called vascular plants. Of course special
manuals and treatments are available for the determination of species in the Thallophyta and Bryophyta
divisions.

CLASSIFICATION OF THE CINNAMON ROSE.

Let us see how the cinnamon rose would fit into
our scheme of classification.

Division - Spermatophyta - the seed plants as
     opposed to the other three divisions.

Subdivision - Angiospermae - plants with seeds
     borne in a closed ovary as opposed to the
     Gymnospermae with naked seeds.

Class - Dicotyledoneae - the plants bearing
     seeds with two cotyledons (instead of one
     as in the Monocotyledoneae).

Order - Rosales - the rose order including the
     rose family with its related families like
     Leguminosae (Legumes).

Family - Rosaceae - the rose family made up of
     roses, apples, etc. Families are usually
     named from some outstanding genus and al-
     most always end in -aceae.

8

Genus - Rosa - the various kinds of roses. As
        it happens this genus gave the name to the
        family and order.

Species - cinnamomea - the Cinnamon Rose.

    Instead of writing out all the above names for
this rose we use only the last two, Rosa cinnamomea
Linnaeus, this constituting what is called the
"scientific, botanical or technical" name of the
plant. Anyone interested in such a name would know
of course that the genus Rosa belongs in the Rosaceae
family, and that this family belongs in the Order
Rosales etc. The author's name (Linnaeus or abbreviated to L.) is a part of the name and ought to be
included especially when absolute accuracy is necessary. Sometimes two people had a hand in naming a
plant and we have a double citation, one of the names
appearing in parenthesis. An example would be Rosa
arkansana variety suffulta (Greene) Cockerell. This
new plant was discovered by Greene and considered by
him to be a new species, Rosa suffulta Greene. But
Cockerell placed it as a variety of Rosa arkansana
Porter, and made a new combination but gave Greene
credit for naming the plant first by placing his name
in parenthesis as indicated.

    Another example would be the name of our peach,
Prunus persica (L.) Batsch. The grand old Swedish
botanist Linnaeus gave it the name Amygdalus persica
L. way back in 1753. But Batsch later decided that
the peach belonged in with the plums and cherries in
the genus Prunus and made the transfer but gave
Linnaeus credit in parenthesis for first giving the
plant its valid specific name.

HOW GENERIC AND SPECIFIC NAMES ORIGINATE.

    It should be of interest to notice how these
scientific names originate. Such a procedure not
only gives a general understanding of the whole subject but also may help us in remembering many of
them should this ever become necessary. As we will
see they are not just a string of meaningless syllables. The following are the most common ways that
scientific names come about.

9

1. Generic names.

    a. In honor of some man, as Lobelia (the lobelias) named for Matthias de l'Obel.
    b. The classical name of the plant, as Verbascum (the mulleins) an old Latin name.
    c. A character of the group as Penstemon (the beard-tongues) from pente - five and stemon - meaning stamen.

2. Specific names.

    a. In honor of a man - Rosa woodsii Lindl. Named for Joseph Wood. Many botanists prefer to start such specific names with a capital letter.
    b. An old classical name - Verbascum thapsus L. - "Thapsus" is a classical name, from ancient Thapsus.
    c. A generic name once used and adapted as a specific name - Saponaria vaccaria L. "Vaccaria" is the old generic name, from "vacca" or cow. Many botanists capitalize the initial letter in such names.
    d. After a locality - Rosa carolina L. from Carolina.
    e. After some characteristic of the species. Rosa cinnamomea L. with fragrance of cinnamon.

CATEGORIES BELOW THE SPECIES.

Botanists have recognized certain strains of plants that stand out by themselves but are not sufficiently distinctive to be considered separate and independent species. Several terminologies have been proposed for these subgroups. A common one is as follows.

1. Varieties. Rosa carolina var. grandiflora (Baker) Rehd. This would be the "large flowered" type of Rosa carolina L. Often such varieties have a separate geographical range. These taxonomic varieties are not to be confused with the horticultural "varieties" of cultivated plants.

10

2. Forma. Saxifraga oppositifolia forma
   albiflora (Lange) Fernald. This would be
   the white flowered type of Saxifraga
   oppositifolia L. which usually has lilac or
   violet flowers. It is used for a minor
   varient, usually represented by a few unusual individuals scattered among the normal
   ones. The botanist's "forma" would corre-
   spond rather closely to the horticulturist's
   "variety". However, another group of
   botanists use the term "subspecies" with
   about the same meaning as "variety" in the
   preceding outline. For example, Erigeron
   glabellus subspecies pubescens (Hook.)
   Cronquist would indicate a major subdivision
   of the species. This is not so confusing
   but unfortunately such workers use "variety"
   about as "forma" was used in the first outline. Erigeron belliastrum var. robustus
   Cronquist would be the robust minor varient
   of the species. This does not especially
   concern the ordinary student who uses one
   manual only. It is hoped that uniformity
   in the nomenclature of these subspecific
   entities will be attained in the near
   future.

The technical names of plants are written in
Latin but often translated from Greek into that
language. However, such names are not pronounced according to the rules used in courses in Latin - at
least in the United States. Instead they are given
an English swing. Some manuals give suggestions on
proper pronunciation but you can expect to find a
great deal of variation among botanists in this respect.

Chapter III

COMMON NAMES AND SCIENTIFIC NAMES

In the preceding chapter we learned that the generic and specific name (with author or authors) constitute the scientific name of the plant. But so called "common names" for certain species have come into more or less general use, especially if the plant is widespread or has some particular interest. "Rose" happens to be the common name of the genus Rosa. Many people will not use any but a common name and may even resent hearing the botanical name. It is important that a student understands the situation concerning plant names exactly, especially if he ever happens to have close contact with the public in general.

VALUES OF COMMON NAMES.

1. They are the only names known and familiar to most people.

2. They are usually simple and relatively easy to remember, usually using words in common use. For example, "Windflower, Mayflower".

3. They are often remarkably descriptive of the plant. For example such names as "Bleeding Heart, Bluebell, Jack-in-the-Pulpit and Dutchman's Breeches", certainly call to mind in clever fashion the appearance of the plants so designated.

WEAKNESSES OF COMMON NAMES.

1. The meaning is clear in only one language.

2. The same plant may have many common names, sometimes by different people in the same area, sometimes in different parts of the country. For example an early spring flower, Pulsatilla ludoviciana (Nutt.) Heller, is known in the writer's circle of acquaintances as both "March Anemone" and "Pasque Flower". A lovely flower of the Rocky Mountain area, Calochortus nuttallii Torr.

is known in Colorado as "Mariposa Lily" but in Utah it has been selected as their state flower under the name of "Sego Lily". Who is to say which is right and which is wrong?

3. The same common name may apply to several plants, both in the same area or in different parts of the country. Names like Mayflower, Bluebell, Soft Maple, Pine and Syringa really have no specific meaning. Even the Irish term "Shamrock" seems to be used for several different species of plants.

4. Common names may actually be ridiculous. For example, "Pineapple" which is not in any way related to either pines or apples "Pepper grass" which is neither a grass or related to pepper, and "Dandelion" which translates "tooth of a lion". Such names do seem inappropriate and may offend some people's sense of logic.

5. Common names have no method or law about them. They rest only on the insecure foundation of general use. Therefore a particular name cannot be called correct and another incorrect. Rather recently an attempt was made to get some order into the situation especially as it applies to horticultural plants. A book called "Standardized Plant Names" was assembled by a committee, listing scientific names followed by a recommended common name. Although a step in the right direction this publication is still incomplete. It has been criticized as being hurriedly assembled and for one reason or another it is not followed by most botanists.

VALUE OF SCIENTIFIC NAMES.

1. They are organized and evaluated according to a definite system of laws and rules. These are passed by an International Congress of Botanical Nomenclature. Several of these conventions have met in the last century, the last one at Paris, France in 1954.

At the present time practically all taxonomists work according to these rules.

2. A plant widely distributed over the world has the same valid scientific name. Not only that but the name is written the same in any country. Reprints of articles written in Japanese for example, have the plant names listed in Roman type and the reader may discover that many of the genera and even some of the species are familiar to him.

3. A plant can have only one valid name. It may have picked up several names along the way but all but the correct one are called "synonyms".

4. Only one plant may have this valid name. Should this name be used through error for a different plant then we call it a "homonym". For example if a new rose species was discovered and named Rosa cinnamomea, this would be an invalid homonym since the name had already been properly used.

5. A scientific name is very often descriptive of the plant, as Penstemon unilateralis Rydb. This means a plant with one-sided flowers (unilateralis) belonging to a group with 5 stamens (Penstemon). Or the name may be of interest historically. In any case it has some kind of meaning providing of course one is familiar with the simple Latin used.

POSSIBLE WEAKNESSES OF SCIENTIFIC NAMES.

1. Only recently has nomenclature been uniform in this country. For many years, up to about 1930, American botanists were using two sets of rules - some followed the International Rules, others the so-called American Rules. This resulted in the different selection of the valid name for about one out of eight cases. Unfortunately some of the existing manuals for plant identification were written in the period before 1930.

14

2. Any law or rule may result in injustice and confusion in specific cases. This does not mean that we must at once do away with law and order entirely.

3. Changes in old familiar names may occur. These are disconcerting and irritating. But one of the rules of nomenclature is that the first name lawfully created must be the valid name. This is called the "law of priority", surely no one would quarrel with its principle. Unfortunately some plant known for years by a botanical name may be found to have been named earlier. We must then abandon the familiar name for an unfamiliar one even though we do not wish to do so. It would hardly do to allow a botanist to make exceptions in certain cases and follow the rules in others. The law itself would soon come to be meaningless.

4. In a few cases the meaning and logic is lost. For example, Linnaeus named 2 species of Convallaria with 2 and 3 leaves on the stem respectively as Convallaria bifolia L. and C. trifolia L. Later on Greene decided these species belonged to the genus Unifolium and used the first recorded specific name. This made the rather startling and certainly illogical combinations, Unifolium bifolium (L.) Greene and Unifolium trifolium (L.) Greene, the 2-leaved and 3-leaved species of a 1-leaved genus! Such cases are of course the exceptions rather than the rule.

Then again many scientific names, such as those named for some little known man or some unfamiliar geographical area may have no meaning at all for the average student and must be learned by rote.

5. Scientific names are often very long and made up of unusual and unfamiliar syllables. This makes it hard for people not trained in classical languages to remember them. However, such names as Geranium, Rhododendron and Chrysanthemum are rather long generic names but because they have come into general use as common names they do

15

not seem particularly difficult for most of us. Some people just will not listen to technical names and may consider you "high hat" or pedantic if you use them, often suspecting you of making an ostentatious display of knowledge.

SUGGESTED COMPROMISE.

If you are talking to people not familiar with scientific names then you must use their language. But take time to explain the situation to them and avoid misunderstandings. For example, they may know the plant by another name than the one you use, and may either privately suspect your identification or attempt to argue the matter with you publicly. Of course it is folly to argue with anyone on the correctness of a common name.

Sometimes it may be judicious to give several common names for the plant but this may often be merely confusing. One can say, "This plant goes by several names but 'Mariposa Lily' seems to be the one more commonly used around here".

If a plant is brought to you for determination it is wise to write down the common and scientific name on a card and hand it to the inquirer. Sometimes such names get into print or at least are passed around by word of mouth. The scientific name will allow other botanists to know exactly what plant it was you checked.

All records of vegetation and all published lists in scientific articles should be in botanical terminology. Even popular articles should have the scientific name of the plant or plants listed somewhere. The writer has read scores of articles, pamphlets and bulletins written about some plant, the exact species of which could not be accurately ascertained from the context.

Many beginners learn the common names of plants and then append to that name the scientific one. If they continue to study plants the process is gradually reversed and they will reason thus, "This plant is a species of Calochortus, oh yes, commonly called Mariposa Lily".

16

Chapter IV

TERMS RELATIVE TO THE FLOWER

PARTS OF A FLOWER.

The flower is the structure most commonly used in classifying and identifying plants. A pear tree (Pyrus sp.), a climbing rose (Rosa sp.) and an herbaceous strawberry (Fragaria sp.) are placed by most botanists in the same family, not because of similarities in general appearance but because their flowers bear a common stamp of the rose family.

Below is a diagram of a typical flower with the parts labeled. Actually the "drawing" is a hypothetical longitudinal section through the flower, with only 2 stamens, 2 petals and 2 sepals shown at the sides. Of course in an actual flower several to many of these structures are usually present in a whorl or circle. Several other diagrams of this nature follow. Almost any possible modification, variation or combination can occur. Fig. 2.

Fig. 2.

FLOWERS IN GENERAL.

1. Anthesis. The period during which the flower parts are open and receptive for pollination.

2. Ephemeral. Lasting for a short time, usually for one day or less.

3. Caducous. Falling off unusually early as compared with similar structures on other plants.

4. Fugacious. Falling off or fading unusually early. About the same as caducous.

5. Marcescent. Withering but persisting and not falling off readily.

17

6. **Many.** Eleven or more. Same as **numerous**. Ordinarily the exact number above 11 has no great taxonomic significance.

7. **Complete** and **Incomplete**. A complete flower has sepals, petals, stamens and pistils present, an incomplete flower lacks one or more of these four parts. The diagrams are hypothetical longitudinal sections of a flower. Fig. 3 and Fig. 4.

COMPLETE FLOWER
Fig. 3.

INCOMPLETE FLOWERS
Fig. 4.

8. **Perfect** (bisexual or hermaphroditic) and **Imperfect** (unisexual). A perfect flower has both stamens and pistils (may or may not have other parts) but an imperfect flower lacks either stamens or pistils. Each diagram shows a longitudinal section of the flower. Fig. 5 and Fig. 6.

PERFECT FLOWERS
Fig. 5.

IMPERFECT FLOWERS
Fig. 6.

9. Staminate and pistillate flowers. A staminate flower lacks a pistil or pistils; a pistillate flower lacks stamens. Petals and sepals may be present or absent.

10. Monoecious. Flowers imperfect (unisexual) with the staminate and pistillate ones on the same plant. An example would be corn (or maize), the "tassel" with staminate flowers, the "ear" with pistillate flowers.

11. Dioecious. Flowers imperfect (unisexual) with the staminate flowers on one plant, the pistillate flowers on another. An example would be a cottonwood tree. Such dioecious plants are often referred to as "male" and "female" individuals.

12. Polygamous. Used by most manuals to mean perfect (bisexual) and imperfect (unisexual) flowers on the same or on different individual plants. The imperfect flowers in such cases are usually staminate.

13. Pedicel. The stalk to an individual flower in an inflorescence. Compare peduncle. Fig. 7.

14. Peduncle. The stalk to an inflorescence or to a solitary flower (like a tulip). See Figure 7 also. Fig. 8.

PEDICEL

PEDUNCLE

PEDUNCLE

FLOWER STALK

FLOWER STALK

Fig. 7.   Fig. 8.

15. Bract. A reduced or modified leaf near a flower or an inflorescence. Very small bracts may be called bractlets. Fig. 9.

BRACT

Fig. 9.

16. **Involucre.** A whorl of distinct or united leaves or bracts subtending (associated with) a flower or an inflorescence. When the involucre appears to be made up of leaves then these are distinctly different in some way from the ordinary leaves below. Fig. 10.

INVOLUCRE

Fig. 10.

17. **Petaloid.** Resembling a petal in some way, usually colored other than green. Often used for sepals or bracts.

INSERTION OF PARTS.

1. **Hypogynous flower.** A flower with sepals and petals (when all are present) attached under the ovary. A longitudinal diagram is given for this and the following three types. Fig. 11.

SUPERIOR OVARY

HYPOGYNOUS FLOWER
Fig. 11.

2. **Epigynous flower.** The other flower parts arise from the summit of an inferior ovary or appear to do so. Fig. 12.

INFERIOR OVARY

EPIGYNOUS FLOWER
Fig. 12.

3. **Perigynous flower.** Borne or arising from around the ovary. Where the stamens or petals (or both) are borne on the edge of a cup-shaped calyx tube or hypanthium. The term "perigynous" is more logically used to describe the insertion of stamens (stamens perigynous) or petals (petals perigynous) rather than applied to the flower as a whole. Fig. 13.

SUPERIOR OVARY

PERIGYNOUS FLOWER
Fig. 13.

4. Ovary partly inferior. Fig. 14.

PARTLY
INFERIOR
OVARY
Fig. 14.

UNION OF PARTS.

1. Connate or distinct. "Connate" means the union
    of like parts (such as petal united to petal);
    "distinct" means like parts not united.

2. Adnate or free. "Adnate" means union of unlike
    parts (as calyx tube to ovary); "free" means un-
    like parts not united.

3. Connivent. Parts in close contact but not act-
    ually united by tissue.

ARRANGEMENT OF PARTS.

1. Imbricate. Partly overlapping DIAGRAM OF A FLOWER
    like shingles on a roof,
    either laterally or vertically.
    One drawing shows the ver-
    tical overlapping, the other
    shows the lateral overlapping
    in cross-section. Fig. 15.

PARTS IMBRICATED
Fig. 15.

2. Valvate. Where the parts come to-
    gether edge to edge but not over-
    lapping. The drawing shows the parts
    in cross-section, like sepals in a
    bud, the structures inside not shown.
    Fig. 16.

PARTS VALVATE
Fig. 16.

CALYX.

    This is usually green and protects or encloses
the petals in the bud. The calyx may be modified or
absent entirely. When only one whorl of the perianth

is present it is always considered to be the calyx even when it is colored (the petals in such a case are considered to be lacking). The calyx segments (sepals) may be persistent as in apple or caducous (very deciduous) as in the bloodroot or prickly poppy.

COROLLA.

This is usually colored and conspicuous. The corolla segments (petals) may be caducous as in the flax, or persistent.

1. Polypetalous. Petals distinct, not united at all to each other. One would expect this word to mean "many petals" but this is not the case. Fig. 17.

POLYPETALOUS
COROLLA
Fig. 17.

2. Claw and blade. Often a single petal narrows to a stalk-like base. Such a stalk is called a "claw" and the expanded portion the "blade". Fig. 18.

CLAW

BLADE
Fig. 18.

3. Sympetalous (or gamopetalous). Petals united at least at the base. Such a corolla may have 3 more or less definite parts as shown on the drawing of a funnelform corolla. (Fig. 19.)

4. Corolla funnelform. Shaped like a funnel. Sympetalous corollas are sometimes divided into a rather cylindrical base called a "tube", a "throat" at the orifice of the tube and a "limb" where the lobes occur. But often this is obscure. Fig. 19.

THROAT   LIMB

TUBE

COROLLA
FUNNELFORM
Fig. 19.

5. Corolla rotate. The tube is short and the throat and limb are abruptly flaring. Fig. 20.

COROLLA
ROTATE
Fig. 20.

6. Corolla campanulate. Bell-shaped. Such flowers may be erect but often hang down as in the drawing. Fig. 21.

COROLLA
CAMPANULATE
Fig. 21.

7. Corolla salverform. With a long tube and abruptly flaring throat and limb. The phlox is an excellent example. Fig. 22.

COROLLA
SALVERFORM
Fig. 22.

8. Corolla cylindrical. Shaped like a cylinder, the sides nearly or quite parallel. This shape is not common. Fig. 23.

COROLLA
CYLINDRICAL
Fig. 23.

9. Regular flower (Actinomorphic). The individual parts of one whorl (like the petals) are all alike. The flower has a radial type of symmetry. Fig. 24.

SEPALS
PETALS
PISTIL
STAMENS
REGULAR FLOWER
Fig. 24.

23

10. Irregular flower (Zygomorphic).
A flower in which the parts of
one whorl (like the petals) are
not alike. The flower has
bilateral symmetry, and may be
2-lipped in its extreme form as
in the figure. Fig. 25.

IRREGULAR FLOWER
Fig. 25.

11. Spur. An elongated structure,
containing nectar, shaped something like the spur of a fight-
ing cock. This spur may be
part of a sepal (as in the drawing) or of a petal. Fig. 26.

SEPAL
SPUR
PEDICEL
PETAL

Fig. 26.

12. Gland. This is a secreting surface or structure, or an appendage having the general appearance
of such an organ. Glands vary
greatly in appearance and general
character. They can be found on
other structures but are often associated with petals. Fig. 27.

GLAND

PETAL WITH GLAND
Fig. 27.

STAMENS.

1. Anther and filament. The anther is
the pollen producing portion, the
filament is the stalk to the anther.
Fig. 28.

ANTHER

FILAMENT

STAMEN
Fig. 28.

2. Anthers basifixed. Attached by one end
to the filament. Fig. 29.

BASIFIXED
ANTHER
Fig. 29.

3. Anthers versatile. Attached to the filament at or near the middle with a "teeter totter" effect. Compare basifixed (Fig. 29).

4. Stamens monadelphous. The stamens are more or less united in one general structure. Fig. 30.

MONADELPHOUS
STAMENS
Fig. 30.

5. Stamens diadelphous. The stamens united in 2 sets. A common example would be most legume flowers, in two sets of 9 and 1 as in the Figure 31.

DIADELPHOUS
STAMENS
Fig. 31.

6. Stamens didynamous. Stamens in 2 sets of unequal length. In the drawing a sympetalous corolla has been split down one side and rolled open; the stamens are inserted on the corolla. Fig. 32.

DIDYNAMOUS
STAMENS
Fig. 32.

7. Stamens tetradynamous. Stamens in 2 sets with 4 longer and 2 shorter. Characteristic of the Cruciferae or Mustard family. In the drawing the sepals and petals are omitted. Fig. 33.

TETRADYNAMOUS
STAMENS
Fig. 33.

25

8. Staminode (staminodium). A sterile
    stamen, for example one lacking an
    anther or a structure resembling
    one, and borne with the stamens.
    The drawing shows 4 ordinary stamens
    and one sterile one (staminode).
    The sepals and petals are omitted.
    Fig. 34.

STERILE
STAMEN

STAMINODE
Fig. 34.

9. Stamen exserted. Protruding
    beyond a surrounding organ,
    usually the corolla. Can be
    used for any 2 structures,
    however. In the drawings the
    stamens and style are ex-
    serted from the corolla.
    Fig. 35. and Fig. 36.

STYLE EXSERTED   STAMENS
Fig. 35.   EXSERTED
                 Fig. 36.

10. Stamens included. Not protruding
    beyond the surrounding structure.
    The corolla in the drawing has
    been split and partially flattened
    out. Fig. 37.

STAMENS
INCLUDED
Fig. 37.

PISTIL.

    There may be one, several or many
pistils to a flower. Usually one can make
out 3 different parts to a pistil, the
stigma, style and ovary. The stigma receives the pollen grains and is often hairy,
roughened or sticky. The ovary bears the
ovules. Fig. 38.

STIGMA

STYLE

OVARY

PISTIL
Fig. 38.

1. Locule. A cell or compartment to an ovary, best
    seen in cross-section. It is not an empty space
    but filled with the attached ovules. The number
    of locules to an ovary has to be ascertained in
    almost every case. This may be somewhat diffi-
    cult to do in a small pistil. The following

suggestions may aid in acquiring the special little knack of sectioning ovaries.

A. Keep the blade very sharp. Many botanists use single edge safety razor blades, discarding the dull ones.

B. Draw the blade through the center of the ovary using a diagonal stroke such as a man may use in shaving with a straight edge razor. Fig. 39.

Fig. 39.

C. Cut a thin slice and let it dry for a minute or two. The succulent ovules will usually shrink and the details of the cells will be plainer.

D. Or cut the ovary in upper and lower halves. Pick out the ovules with a needle from one of the cut surfaces. This will show up the structural details within. Rotating the half ovary with some pressure may squeeze out the still attached ovules and give the same effect.

E. Try to find a partly developed fruit. An ovary in its enlargement to the fruit ordinarily does not change in its internal structure. The parts are merely larger and easier to study.

27

2. Septum. This is the wall between the locules. At its outer limits it runs into the ovary wall. Fig. 40.

OVARY WALL
SEPTUM
OVARY WALL & SEPTUM
Fig. 40.

3. Ovary wall. The outer wall of the ovary. (Fig. 40.)

4. Placentae. The place or part of an ovary where the ovules are attached. Four types of placentation are most common.

A. Parietal. Ovules attached at the outer wall of the ovary which is almost always one-celled. The drawings include a cross-section of the ovary. Fig. 41.

3 PARIETAL PLACENTAE
Fig. 41.

B. Axile. Ovary 2- or more-celled with the ovules attached at the center. Each drawing shows a cross-section of an ovary. Fig. 42.

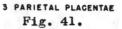

AXILE PLACENTAE
Fig. 42.

C. Basal. The ovules attached at the base of the one-celled ovary. The drawing shows an ovary in longitudinal section with one ovule. Fig. 43.

BASAL
PLACENTA
Fig. 43.

28

D. Free-central. The ovules
borne on a central column a-
rising from the base of a one-
celled ovary. This central
column may be made up (at
least in part) of several
fused placentae. A cross-
section of the ovary is shown
in the drawing to the right.
Fig. 44.

FREE CENTRAL
PLACENTA
Fig. 44.

5. Sporophyll. A spore bearing leaf
in the non-flowering plants.
Sepals and petals are thought to
be sterile sporophylls, stamens
and pistils are modified sporophylls. The drawing suggests how
a sporophyll could have rolled up
to form an anther in the evolutionary development of a stamen.
Fig. 45.

SPOROPHYLL
COMPARED TO ANTHER
Fig. 45.

    The following drawing
indicates how a sporophyll
could have rolled up to
form a pistil. Such a
pistil would have one carpel only. Fig. 46.

THEORETICAL
RELATIONSHIP OF
SPOROPHYLL TO   SPOROPHYLL
OVARY   ROLLING IN
Fig. 46.
Part 1   Part 2

29

6. Carpel. That part of a pistil formed from one sporophyll in the evolutionary development of the flower. The number of carpels is obtained by counting the stigma lobes, the styles, the locules and the placentae. The highest number will be the number of carpels. (Various degrees of fusion occur.) However, some placentae are double or paired as in Fig. 47 but are still counted as one. Fig. 47 and Fig. 48.

I CARPEL—
I PAIRED PLACENTA

2 CARPELS—
2 STYLES

Fig. 47.

2 CARPELS—
2 LOCULES
2 PLACENTAE

2 CARPELS—
2 PLACENTAE

Fig. 48.

7. Simple ovary. An ovary formed from one sporophyll, as in drawing number 47 (left figure). Simple ovaries are often more than one to a flower.

8. Compound ovary. An ovary formed from two or more sporophylls, as in drawing number 47 (right figure) and 48 (both figures).

30

Chapter V

TERMS RELATIVE TO THE INFLORESCENCE

Often flowers are grouped in variously arranged clusters called inflorescences. The more common terms relative to these inflorescences are discussed below.

1. Indeterminate (racemose or centrifugal). In this type the young flowers (or even primordial tissue) are at the end of the main axis, or in the case of the umbel in the center, while the older flowers are below or to the outside. In such an inflorescence it is sometimes possible to find buds at the top, mature flowers at the middle and fruit at the base of the main axis. It is called "indeterminate" because it is theoretically possible for such an inflorescence to continue developing new flowers at the tip for an indeterminate length of time. Actually in most cases development stops rather soon.

2. Determinate (cymose or centripetal). Here the oldest flower is at the end of the main axis with the younger flowers arising from below. Sometimes when the rachis is non-existent, as in an unusual umbel, the central flowers may be older with the outer flowers younger. Such a case would be a special type of "determinate" inflorescence. The cyme is the only example of this type.

3. Spike. An indeterminate type of inflorescence with the flowers perfect and sessile along the main axis (rachis). Fig. 49

SPIKE
Fig. 49.

4. Raceme. An indeterminate type of inflorescence with the flowers single on pedicels arranged along an elongated rachis. When the pedicels are very short and the flowers crowded the raceme resembles a spike at first glance and is called "spike-like". Fig. 50.

Fig. 50.

5. Panicle. An indeterminate type of inflorescence with 2 or more flowers on each branch, these arranged on an elongated axis (usually called a "rachis" or a "main axis"). Fig. 51.

PANICLE
Fig. 51.

6. Corymb. An indeterminate flat-topped inflorescence. It is essentially a raceme with the lower pedicels elongated and the rachis more or less shortened. Fig. 52.

SIMPLE CORYMB
Fig. 52.

A corymb can be compound, with several corymb-like clusters, these in turn crowded into a larger, collective corymb. Fig. 53.

COMPOUND CORYMB
Fig. 53.

7. <u>Umbel</u>. An indeterminate type of flat-topped
or orbicular inflores-
cence with the rachis
non-existent. Fig. 54
and Fig. 55.

FLAT TOP UMBEL   ROUNDED UMBEL
Fig. 54.   Fig. 55.

Umbels can be compound as in
Fig. 56.

COMPOUND UMBEL
Fig. 56.

8. <u>Head</u>. A dense
cluster of usually
indeterminate, ses-
sile or nearly sessile
flowers (or fruits)
on a very short axis.
It is used especially
for the involucrate
inflorescence in the
Compositae family.
Fig. 57 and Fig. 58.

CLOVER   SUNFLOWER
HEAD   HEAD
Fig. 57.   Fig. 58.

Figure 59 is a longitud-
inal section of Figure
58.

HEAD
DISK FLOWERS
RAY
FLOWER
INVOLUCRE
Fig. 59.

33

9. <u>Cyme</u>. A determinate inflorescence. It may be of various shapes or degrees of branching but the oldest flower is always on the end of the branch. Fig. 60.

TYPES OF CYMES
Fig. 60.

10. <u>Glomerule</u>. A general term for a densely packed cluster of flowers.

11. <u>Scorpioid</u>. An inflorescence of one-sided flowers coiled at the apex like the tail of a scorpion. Fig. 61.

SCORPIOID RACEME
Fig. 61.

12. <u>Thyrse</u>. A cylindrical or ovoid-pyramidal, usually densely flowered panicle on the order of a cluster of grapes or a lilac inflorescence. Fig. 62.

THYRSE
Fig. 62.

13. <u>Spadix</u>. A spike with a thick and fleshy central axis, usually densely flowered with imperfect flowers. Such an inflorescence is often subtended by a large bract called a <u>spathe</u>. Fig. 63.

SPATHE

STAMINATE FLOWERS

SPADIX—

PISTILLATE FLOWERS

SPADIX & SPATHE
Fig. 63.

34

14.   **Ament** or **catkin**. A spike or spike-like inflorescence made up of unisexual flowers. Willows, poplars and cottonwoods are plants bearing aments. Fig. 64.

AMENT
OR CATKIN
Fig. 64.

15.   **Solitary**. Flowers borne singly, not in clusters. These may be terminal or axillary as indicated in the drawing. Fig. 65.

SOLITARY

TERMINAL
FLOWERS

SOLITARY

AXILLARY
FLOWERS

Fig. 65.

PANICLE OF CYMES

16.   **Combinations**. Sometimes the flowers are borne in inflorescences whose general nature is one type but the individual parts are of another. A combination term may be necessary like the one figured. Fig. 66.

Fig. 66.

Chapter VI

TERMS RELATIVE TO UNDERGROUND PARTS

The specific and even the generic differences of plants are often based on underground characters. Every specimen of a herbaceous plant ought to indicate either by the actual material or by notes on the label any underground character that might be of value in identifying material in that particular group. Some characteristic structures of that type are as follows.

1. Taproot. A thick tapering root, on the order of a beet or carrot root. A taproot may be thick as in the drawing or relatively slender. Fig. 67.

TAP ROOT
Fig. 67.

2. Tuber. A thickened subterranean stem typically with numerous buds (eyes) like a potato. Fig. 68.

TUBER
Fig. 68.

3. Bulb. A subterranean bud having fleshy scales like an onion. The drawing shows the bulb in longitudinal section. Fig. 69.

BULB
Fig. 69.

4. Corm. A vertical, thickened, solid underground stem such as borne by a crocus or gladiolus. Fig. 70.

CORM
(SOLID CENTER)
Fig. 70.

5. Rhizome. A prostrate more or less horizontally elongated stem growing partly or completely beneath the surface of the ground, usually rooting at the nodes and becoming up-curved at the apex. Sometimes called a "rootstock". The scales on the drawing are actually modified leaves. Fig. 71.

RHIZOME
SCALES
SCAR OF SCALE
ROOTS
Fig. 71.

6. Annual root. A root that develops with the stem for the season and dies with it at the end of that season. It is seldom much enlarged, has no special food storage structures and usually merges into the stem without a break caused by scars or constrictions. (See perennial root discussion.) The scars of the cotyledons may show as indicated on the drawing and the early leaves may wither or drop leaving scars on the basal part of the stem. Fig. 72.

COTYLEDON
SCARS
Fig. 72.

7. Perennial root. One that lives over winter and initiates the stem growth from buds. In a woody plant these buds are borne above the ground, in a herbaceous perennial plant they are produced at or near the ground level. Such a root must be large enough to store enough food to start the new growth in the spring. Fig. 73.

SEASONS SHOOT
LAST SEASONS SHOOT
ROOT
Fig. 73.

Sometimes perennial roots become horizontally elongated and
spread the plant on the order of
rhizomes, but rhizomes have reduced leaves (scales) or scars
where the scales dropped away.
True roots lack such structures.
Fig. 74.

SPREADING ROOTS
Fig. 74.

8. Annual and perennial plants.

    (1)   Woody plants are always perennial ones.

    (2)   Plants with special organs for food storage
such as tubers, bulbs, corms, rhizomes,
etc., are perennial.

    (3)   Plants with large roots are usually peren-
nial.

    (4)   Plants with remnants of last year's stem
attached to the crown or roots are perennial plants (See Fig. 73). Be careful your
specimen isn't an annual plant late in the
season where the early stem has been cut
off. In such a case this old stem may by
contrast look old and weathered but the new
sprouts from near the base will be green
and fresh looking.

    (5)   Plants with enlarged crowns near the ground
level, these having a series of scars or
constrictions as they enter up into the
stem, are perennials. The buds on the
crown send up the new stems and a "break"
is almost always apparent where these develop.

An excellent way to develop this concept is to
check the annual or perennial character of every
plant identified as it is listed in the manual after
identification, even though that character might not
have been needed in running it through the key. Then
look carefully at the underground parts of the specimen to see how it squares up with the record.

38

Chapter VII

TERMS RELATIVE TO THE STEM

Only the more common terms are discussed below. The ones relative to the angle of the stem as compared to the horizontal ground level are sometimes loosely used.

1. Caulescent. Having a leafy stem above the ground. The leaves can be any shape or in any arrangement. Fig. 75.

ACAULESCENT   CAULESCENT
Fig. 75.

2. Acaulescent. The leaves clustered at or near the base of the plant. The leafless stalk is called a scape and the plant is described as scapose (having a scape). (See Fig. 75).

3. Strict. A stem rigidly upright. Fig. 76.

STRICT
STEM
Fig. 76.

4. Prostrate. A stem lying flat on the ground, often rooting at the nodes but otherwise not particularly differentiated. Fig. 77.

PROSTRATE
STEM
Fig. 77.

5. Decumbent. A stem reclining on the ground but turned upward near the end. Fig. 78.

DECUMBENT
STEM
Fig. 78.

6. Ascending. A stem growing obliquely upward at about a 40 - 60 degree angle from the horizontal, often curved as shown on the drawing. Fig. 79.

ASCENDING
STEM
Fig. 79.

7. Caespitose. Stems growing in tufts or rather close clusters. The term is rather loosely used by some authors. Also written cespitose. Fig. 80.

CAESPITOSE
STEM
Fig. 80.

8. Stolon. A specialized stem trailing on the ground and rooting at the nodes. A stolon intergrades with a prostrate stem. Fig. 81.

STOLON
Fig. 81.

9. Runner. A very slender stolon, sometimes limited to those that root only at the apex. Fig. 82.

RUNNER
Fig. 82.

40

10. Herbaceous. A stem that is not woody like those of trees and shrubs. This term is also used to describe a structure green in color (like the herbage).

11. Woody. A perennial stem that has had time to produce woody tissue, a characteristic bark which is often gray to tan and buds that produce the next season's growth. Sometimes a stem may be woody only at the very base of the plant.

Chapter VIII

TERMS RELATIVE TO THE LEAVES

Differences in leaf characters are often utilized in separating the species of a genus. Sometimes they are used to differentiate between larger units such as the genera in a family. The terms relative to leaf surfaces are treated in Chapter IX.

GENERAL TERMS.

1. Deciduous. Leaves all falling at the end of the growing season or at least withering up and becoming lifeless. Usually a corky layer called the "abscission layer" develops at the base of the petiole, effectively walling off the leaf. When the abscission layer does not split apart, the dead leaf may remain on the stem over part or all the resting period. Fig. 83.

BLADE
PETIOLE
ABSCISSION LAYER
DECIDUOUS LEAF
Fig. 83.

The term "deciduous" is also used for any part that falls away rather early in comparison with the situation for most similar parts.

2. Evergreen. Bearing green leaves throughout the year. Evergreen leaves in most parts of the United States are usually needle-shaped like those on a spruce or pine. Such leaves are not permanent structures of course, and are eventually shed, but some at least remain on the tree all winter.

ARRANGEMENT ON THE STEM.

This refers to the particular way the leaves are inserted on the stem.

1. **Opposite.** Two leaves inserted opposite each other on the stem. Fig. 84.

Fig. 84.

2. **Alternate.** Only one leaf inserted at a node. Fig. 85.

Fig. 85.

3. **Whorled (or verticillate).** With three or more leaves inserted at one node. Fig. 86.

LEAVES WHORLED
Fig. 86.

4. **Radical.** The leaves arise from or very near the root. When the leaves are rather numerous they form what is called a "rosette". Fig. 87.

LEAVES RADICAL
Fig. 87.

43

5. Basal. The leaves tend to crowd down toward the base of the stem. The term is not very exact but is convenient. Most basal leaves are essentially alternate. Fig. 88.

LEAVES BASAL
Fig. 88.

6. Equitant. Leaves that are folded or flattened so that the two edges are turned toward and away from the stem. Fig. 89.

LEAVES EQUITANT
Fig. 89.

SIMPLE AND COMPOUND LEAVES.

A simple leaf is one with only one definite segment present between the stem and the end of the blade. It may be variously lobed. Fig. 90 and Fig. 91.

SIMPLE   SIMPLE
Fig. 90.Fig. 91.

A compound leaf has definite and distinct segments (leaflets) from the stem to the apex. The most common types are pinnately and palmately compound. Fig. 92 and Fig. 93.

PINNATELY COMPOUND
Fig. 92.

PALMATE
Fig. 93.

44

The common fault in judging simple or compound leaves is to mistake a leaflet for a leaf and consider the leaf rachis to be a stem. However, the majority of compound leaves have a leaflet directly on the end of the rachis. A stem never has a leaf on the end but terminates in a growing point, which may be active or inactive. If this growing area is active then young leaves will be present. Fig. 94 and Fig. 95.

TWIG
WOODY STEM
SIMPLE LEAVES

Fig. 94.

NO BUD
PETIOLE
RACHIS
BUD
TWIG
WOODY STEM-COMPOUND LEAF

Fig. 95.

There may be a bud present at the base of a leaf but never at the base of a leaflet. This is particularly noticeable in plants with woody twigs. The buds may not develop in some herbaceous plants or may produce side branches. Sometimes young shoots are mistakenly considered to be compound leaves especially when the old subtending leaf has withered away. Fig. 96.

MAIN STEM
GROWING POINT
BRANCH LEAF
OLD LEAF

Fig. 96.

1. Decompound. A leaf that is divided once and at least once again. Examples figured can be found under bipinnate, tripinnate and biternate (Figs. 97, 98 and 100).

45

2. Bipinnate. A decompound leaf, pinnately compound with the main divisions once again compound. Fig. 97.

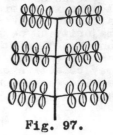

Fig. 97.

3. Tripinnate. A leaf that is three times pinnate. Fig. 98.

Fig. 98.

4. Ternate. A compound leaf with 3 equal divisions; palmately compound with 3 leaflets. Fig. 99.

TERNATE
Fig. 99.

5. Biternate. A decompound leaf ternate with each main division once again ternate. Fig. 100.

BITERNATE
Fig. 100.

6. Pinnatifid. A simple leaf but cut
   ~~very deep~~ in pinnate fashion.
   Fig. 101.

PINNATIFID
Fig. 101.

7. Fern leaf. The fern leaf (frond)
   ~~has been~~ given special terms as
   indicated below. The actual stems
   of our ordinary ferns are at or
   below the ground level.
   Fig. 102.

FERN FROND
Fig. 102.

SHAPE.

   This is the general outline of
the leaf, usually disregarding the tip
and base. When the leaf is lobed, the
general outline cuts off the lobes and
fills in the sinuses. Fig. 103.

OVATE
Fig. 103.

1. Needle-shaped (acerose). Very narrow like the leaves of spruce or fir. Such leaves may be terete, quadrangular or flattened in cross-section. Fig. 104.

NEEDLE SHAPED
Fig. 104.

2. Awl-shaped. This is a rather small, narrowly triangular shape like the leaves on some of the Red Cedars or Junipers. Fig. 105.

AWL SHAPED
Fig. 105.

3. Linear. A narrow flat shape with parallel sides. The length is over 4 times the width. Fig. 106.

LINEAR
Fig. 106.

4. Lanceolate. A narrow leaf broadest nearer the base. Fig. 107.

5. Ovate. Egg-shaped and connected at the broader end. Fig. 108.

LANCEOLATE
Fig. 107.

OVATE
Fig. 108.

6. Oblanceolate. Lanceolate but connected by the narrower end. Fig. 109.

7. Obovate. Ovate in shape but connected at the narrower end. Fig. 110.

OBLANCEOLATE   OBOVATE
Fig. 109. Fig. 110

8. Oblong. Two to four times longer than wide, the sides parallel or nearly so. Fig. 111.

9. Oval. Broadest at the middle and the width over half the length. This term is loosely used in some manuals. Fig. 112.

OBLONG   OVAL
Fig. 111.Fig. 112.

10. Elliptic (or elliptical). Broadest at the middle, the ends rather equal. This is another term that is very loosely used but the length is at least twice the width. The drawings show a broadly elliptic and a rather narrowly elliptic leaf. Fig. 113.

ELLIPTIC
Fig. 113.

11. Spatulate. Flattened spoon-shaped, connected at the narrow tapered end. Shaped like the old fashioned "spatula". Fig. 114.

12. Deltoid. Triangular like the Greek letter "Delta". The blade is usually connected to the petiole at the middle of one side. Fig. 115.

SPATULATE   DELTOID
Fig. 114. Fig. 115.

49

13. Orbicular (round). A flat object of round shape like a dinner plate. A round object in 3 dimensions would be globose.

14. Falcate. Curved and tapering upward like a scimitar, hence asymmetric. Fig. 116.

FALCATE
Fig. 116.

15. Reniform. Kidney-shaped, usually connected at the sinus. Fig. 117.

16. Peltate. A leaf, usually broad in shape with the blade connected to the petiole part way in from the margin, giving an opened umbrella-like effect in its extreme form. Fig. 118.

RENIFORM   PELTATE
Fig. 117.   Fig. 118.

17. Cordate. A broadly heart-shaped leaf connected at its broader end. It is really a broadly ovate shape with the base heart-shaped. Fig. 119.

    An obcordate leaf would be the same except attached at the narrower end. Fig. 120.

CORDATE   OBCORDATE
Fig. 119.Fig. 120

18. Sagittate. A leaf with arrow-like base, the lobes pointed backward. Fig. 121.

19. Hastate (Halberd-shaped). Shaped like a conventional arrowhead but the basal lobes flaring out. Fig. 122.

SAGITTATE   HASTATE
Fig. 121.Fig. 122.

BASE.

1. Rounded. The sides of the leaf
   rounded into the petiole. One
   figure has a broadly rounded base,
   the other a rather narrowly rounded one. Fig. 123.

ROUNDED
Fig. 123.

2. Cuneate. Base wedge-shaped, sometimes spoken of as "acute". One
   base in the drawings is broadly
   cuneate, the other is rather narrowly so. Fig. 124.

CUNEATE
Fig. 124.

3. Truncate. Base squared
   as if cut off by a
   straight blade.
   Fig. 125.

TRUNCATE
Fig. 125.

4. Oblique. The two sides
   markedly uneven at base.
   Most such leaf bases are
   cuneate on one side and
   rounded or cordate on the
   other. Fig. 126.

LEAF BASES

5. Cordate. Base shaped
   like that of the conventional valentine heart.
   Fig. 127.

OBLIQUE   CORDATE
Fig. 126.   Fig. 127.

6. Sagittate. Lobed at base,
   the lobes pointing backward.
   Sometimes used as a term for
   general shape. See Fig. 121.
   Fig. 128.

7. Hastate. Lobed at base, the
   lobes flaring. See Fig. 122.
   Fig. 129.

SAGITTATE   HASTATE
Fig. 128. Fig. 129.

APEX.

This refers only to the general area of the tip.

1. Acuminate. Pointed with the two margins somewhat pinched in before joining at the extreme tip. The extreme tip may be broad and short or long and narrow as indicated. Fig. 130.

ACUMINATE LEAF TIPS

ABRUPT   BROADLY   NARROW

Fig. 130.

2. Acute. Pointed but the two margins straight until they meet. The leaf may be broadly or narrowly acute. Fig. 131.

ACUTE LEAF TIPS

BROADLY   MEDIUM   NARROW

Fig. 131.

3. Obtuse. The tip rounded at the extreme end. Fig. 132.

4. Rounded. Apex broadly round, really no leaf tip present at all. Some manuals may call this "broadly obtuse". Fig. 133.

OBTUSE   ROUNDED

Fig. 132 Fig.133

5. Cuspidate. With an abrupt, short sharp firm point. Compare "mucronate". Fig. 134.

6. Mucronate. With an abrupt short tip but this not sharp. Many manuals make no distinction between this and "cuspidate". Fig. 135.

CUSPIDATE

MUCRONATE

Fig. 134. Fig. 135.

7. Aristate. With an awn or stiff bristle at apex. If the awn is small the apex may be called "aristulate". Fig. 136.

8. Apiculate. Ending in an abrupt slender tip which is not stiff. Fig. 137.

ARISTATE   APICULATE

Fig. 136. Fig. 137

52

9. Truncate. The tip appearing cut off by a straight
blade. Fig. 138.

TRUNCATE   EMARGINATE

10. Emarginate. Having a
shallow notch at the broad
apex. See "retuse".
Fig. 139.

Fig. 138.   Fig. 139.
RETUSE

11. Retuse. A shallow notch on a rounded
apex. Many manuals do not make a distinction between this and "emarginate".
Fig. 140.

Fig. 140.

MARGINS

1. Entire. No teeth or
lobes on the margins.
Fig. 141.

2. Repand (undulate).
A gently wavy margin.
Fig. 142.

3. Sinuate. Wavy with
more pronounced undu-
lations. Fig. 143.

ENTIRE   REPAND   SINUATE
Fig. 141. Fig. 142. Fig. 143.

4. Serrate. Toothed with the
teeth directed forward toward the apex of the leaf.
Very small teeth may be called serrulate. Fig. 144.

5. Doubly serrate. With
larger serrate teeth, these
in turn bearing small ser-
rations. Fig. 145.

SERRATE   DOUBLE
           SERRATE
Fig. 144. Fig. 145.

6. Dentate. Toothed but the teeth pointing
outward at right angles to the midline
of the leaf. Such teeth are usually
larger than serrate and some manuals
may loosely call all large teeth
"dentate". Small dentate teeth would be
called "denticulate". Fig. 146.

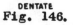
DENTATE
Fig. 146.

7. Crenate. Toothed with the teeth
    <u>rounded</u> at their apex. Fig. 147.

CRENATE
Fig. 147.

8. Incised. Leaf cut sharp-
    <u>ly and</u> usually irregular-
    ly, with sharp sinuses,
    deeper than teeth but
    seldom as deep as one-
    half way in to the mid-
    rib or base. Fig. 148.

INCISED MARGINS
Fig. 148.

9. Cleft. Margin cut in
    <u>about</u> one-half way in to
    the midrib or base, es-
    pecially when the sinus
    is sharp. Fig. 149.

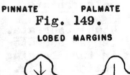

PINNATE   PALMATE
Fig. 149.

10. Lobed. This is often a
    <u>loose</u>ly used term but
    technically it means cut in
    not over one-half way in to
    the midrib or base with the
    sinuses and tips of the seg-
    ments rounded. A lobed
    margin often intergrades with
    one sinuate. Fig. 150.

LOBED MARGINS

PINNATE   PALMATE
Fig. 150.

11. <u>Parted</u>. The margins are cut in over one-half way to the midrib or base. The sinuses may be sharp or rounded.

PARTED LEAF MARGINS

PINNATE   PALMATE

Fig. 151.

12. <u>Divided</u>. Cut in to the midrib or to the base. A divided leaf is nearly compound but the segments do not form definite units or leaflets. Fig. 152.

DIVIDED LEAF MARGINS

PINNATE   PALMATE

Fig. 152.

VENATION.

1. <u>Parallel</u>. The veins are small and run more or less parallel, all are about the same size (except sometimes the central one), and the small connections between them are obscure. Most parallel-veined leaves are long and narrow. Fig. 153.

PARALLEL
Fig.153.

2. Netted (reticulated). The veins
    are large and small, the small
    ones connecting to each other to
    form a net. (The minute con-
    nections are not shown on the
    drawing.) Fig. 154.

3. Pinnately veined. With one
    larger midvein and smaller
    veins coming off along its
    length. Fig. 155.

NET   PINNATE

Fig. 154. Fig. 155.

4. Palmately veined. With 2 or more
    large veins arising at or very near
    the base of the leaf blade. Such
    leaves are usually rather broad.
    Fig. 156.

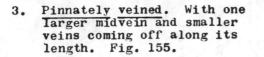

PALMATE

Fig. 156.

56

Chapter IX

TERMS RELATIVE TO SURFACES

The following terms are the ones most commonly
applied to the surface of a leaf, usually the under
side when no special designation is made since that
is the surface that is most apt to be unusual and
distinctive. Such terms usually refer either to the
lack of hairs or to the particular type of hairs
present. Often specific differentiations are based
wholly or in part on variations in these surfaces.
The terms relative to leaf surfaces are usually considered to be the most difficult of all descriptive
terms to master. For example, what is a "long"
hair, and how long does it have to be before it
ceases to be a "short" hair? Such a question cannot
be answered with a concrete measurement.

One way of securing these necessary concepts is
to make a practice of checking the surface description as it may be recorded for the plant in the
manual, even though such surface characters may not
have been needed in the identification. Then compare
that description with your specimen. An even better
method is to collect several or many outstanding
types of different surfaces, try to diagnose each in
the following key. Then if at all possible have
your examples checked by an expert.

Key to Common Leaf Surfaces
(usually lower)

1. Without hairs or projections

    2. Surface sticky------------------<u>viscid</u> (1.)

    2. Surface not sticky

        3. Waxy, usually glandular
           coat---------------------<u>glaucous</u> (2.)
                                 (<u>pruinose</u>)

        3. Not waxy   <u>glabrous</u> (3.)

1. With hairs or projections

    4. Hairs on apex or margin only, or these es-
       pecially noticeable

        5. Hairs at apex only, long, in
           a tuft----------------------<u>comose</u> (4.)

        5. Hairs on margins------------<u>ciliate</u> (5.)

    4. Hairs or projections scattered on leaf

        6. With short, rough hairs or covered with
           scales

           7. Short rough hairs or rough
               projections------------<u>scabrous</u> (6.)

           7. With scales--------------<u>scurfy</u> (7.)

        6. Hairs short or long but not short and
          rough

           8. Hairs barbed or hooked

               9. Hairs hooked at tip-<u>uncinate</u> (8.)

               9. Hairs barbed

10. Hairs barbed only at
tip-------------------------glochidiate (9.)

10. Hairs barbed down sides-----barbellate (10.)

8. Hairs not barbed or hooked

    11. Hairs radially branched or several
        arising and spreading from a
        common center-----------------stellate (11.)

    11. Hairs not branching, not arranged
        as above

        12. Hairs curled and interwoven

            13. Very fine and short,
                white--------------canescent (12.)

            13. Medium to long

                14. Hairs in scattered
                    patches-------floccose (13.)

                14. Hairs evenly distributed

                    15. Hairs medium to
                        short----tomentose (14.)

                    15. Hairs long--lanate (15.)

        12. Hairs fairly straight

            16. Tipped with pinhead-like
                glands------------glandular (16.)

            16. No pinhead-like glands

                17. Hairs appressed usually in
                    one direction and either
                    short and stiff or long and
                    silky

                    18. Short, stiff--
                            strigose (17.)

                    18. Long, silky--
                            sericeous (18.)

17. Hairs not appressed (or if so not
    short and stiff or long and silky as
    above)

    19. Soft short to medium hairs

        20. Very short-<u>puberulent</u> (19.)

        20. Short to
            medium------<u>pubescent</u> (20.)

    19. Hairs long

        21. Hairs soft

            22. Shaggy
                hairs----<u>villous</u> (21.)

            22. Hairs not
                shaggy----<u>pilose</u> (22.)

        21. Hairs moderately to very
            stiff

            23. Moderately
                stiff----<u>hirsute</u> (23.)

            23. Very
                stiff-----<u>hispid</u> (24.)

TYPES OF SURFACES.

    The 24 terms included in the key are explained
below and a figure is attempted for most of them.
Do not place too much reliance on the drawings since
it is almost impossible to give an adequate idea of
the types of hairs by a figure. The hairs are drawn
in relative size to each other.

1. <u>Viscid</u>. Sticky, as if covered with a thin layer
   of syrup. The sticky covering may harden in age
   but such a leaf will have small particles of
   dust, debris, etc., adhering to its surface.

2. <u>Glaucous</u>. Covered with a waxy, usually whitish
   covering. This should rub off showing the green
   of the leaf cells below, but some manuals use
   the term for any whitish surface. The word

60

"pruinose" means about the same, often used to designate a conspicuous glaucous covering. An inconspicuous glaucous covering would be "glaucescent".

3. Glabrous. No hairs of any kind present or any other unusual characteristic. A surface that loses its hairs readily and soon becomes glabrous is called "glabrate" or "glabrescent".

4. Comose. With long hairs in a tuft at the apex, the scattered hairs if present at all, much shorter. This term is usually used for seeds. Such a tuft of hairs is called a "coma". Fig. 157.

Fig. 157.

5. Ciliate. Beset with a marginal fringe of hairs. Other hairs may be present but are much less conspicuous. When the hairs are coarse and crowded the condition may be called "fimbriate". Fig. 158.

Fig. 158.

6. Scabrous. Rough and rasp-like when gently rubbed with the finger tip. This roughness may be caused by short, stiff hairs or short sharp projections. Fig. 159.

Fig. 159.

7. Scurfy. Surface covered with small, often overlapping scale-like particles. These are usually definite enough to be seen with a hand lens. Fig. 160.

Fig. 160.

61

8. Uncinate. Stiff hairs or bristles hooked at the apex, usually used for the surfaces of fruits instead of for leaves. Fig. 161.

UNCINATE

GLOCHIDIATE

9. Glochidiate. Stiff hairs or bristles barbed at the apex. Fig. 162.

Fig. 161. Fig. 162.

10. Barbellate. Stiff hairs or bristles barbed down the sides (usually at apex too). Fig. 163.

BARBELLATE

Fig. 163.

11. Stellate. Star-like or star-shaped with slender segments or hairs radiating out from a common center. Fig. 164.

STELLATE HAIRS

Fig. 164.

CANESCENT

12. Canescent. The surface more or less densely covered with white or gray short hairs, giving that color to the surface. The term is sometimes loosely used to mean any gray or white surface. Fig. 165.

Fig. 165.

FLOCCOSE

13. Floccose. Surface with medium to long interwoven hairs, these occurring in scattered patches. Fig. 166.

Fig. 166.

14. Tomentose. Covered with interwoven short to medium length hairs, this covering usually dense enough to conceal the true leaf surface. Fig. 167.

TOMENTOSE

LANATE

15. Lanate. With interwoven long hairs. Fig. 168.

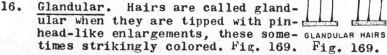

Fig. 167.   Fig. 168.

16. Glandular. Hairs are called glandular when they are tipped with pinhead-like enlargements, these sometimes strikingly colored. Fig. 169.

GLANDULAR HAIRS
Fig. 169.

17. Strigose. With appressed rather short and stiff hairs. When the hairs are very short the surface would be called "strigillose". Fig. 170.

STRIGOSE

Fig. 170.

18. Sericeous. Covered with long straight soft, appressed hairs giving a silky effect. The hairs are more numerous than indicated on the drawing. Fig. 171.

SERICEOUS
Fig. 171.

19. Puberulent. With very short hairs. Fig. 172.

PUBERULENT

Fig. 172.

20. **Pubescent.** With short to medium length hairs. This term is sometimes used to mean with hairs of any type. Fig. 173.

PUBESCENT
Fig. 173.

21. **Villous.** With long soft, somewhat wavy hairs. Fig. 174.

VILLOUS

Fig. 174.

22. **Pilose.** With long, soft, nearly straight hairs. Many manuals do not differentiate this term from "villous". Fig. 175.

PILOSE
Fig. 175.

23. **Hirsute.** With long moderately stiff hairs. A less pronounced hirsute condition may be called "hirsutulous" (or hirsutulose). Fig. 176.

HIRSUTE

Fig. 176.

24. **Hispid.** With long very stiff hairs, these usually sharp and stiff enough to penetrate the skin of the hands. A less pronounced hispid condition may be called "hispidulous". Fig. 177.

HISPID

Fig. 177.

Chapter X

GENERAL TERMS

This chapter explains terms that are in common use but did not seem to fit in any other place.

1. Tendril. A slender modified stem or leaf, commonly coiling at the apex and
serving as an organ of support. Fig. 178.

TENDRILS

STEM MODIFIED PETIOLE
       LEAF
Fig. 178.

2. Aquatic plant. A plant that must live partly or
entirely in water for at least part of its life
cycle. A true aquatic plant often has a weak
flaccid stem and dissected leaves.

3. Terrestrial. A plant growing in the air with its
basal parts in wet or dry soil.

4. Fern-like. A plant with filmy-dissected leaves
on the general order of those of a fern plant.
See Fig. 102.

5. Rush-like. A grass-like
plant with very small inconspicuous flowers and typical
long linear grass-like leaves.
The drawing to the right shows
a flower split longitudinally
and only one-half indicated.
Fig. 179.

RUSH
Fig. 179.

6. Grass-like. A
    grass-like plant
    with long linear
    grass-like
    leaves and very
    inconspicuous
    flowers. The
    round drawing to
    the right shows
    a grass stem
    (culm) in cross-
    section surround-
    ed by a leaf
    sheath. Fig. 180.

7. Moss-like. Re-
    sembling the com-
    mon moss plant,
    with rather short
    and slender stems
    crowded with
    small thin leaves.
    The drawing shows
    2 spore-bearing
    capsules of a moss
    plant. Fig. 181.

MOSS
Fig. 181.

GRASS
Fig. 180.

8. Heath-like. Re-
    sembling a heath,
    with thick, small,
    entire-margined
    leaves, these
    often partly roll-
    ed. Fig. 182.

HEATH LIKE

SECTION OF LEAF
Fig. 182.

VINE

9. Vine. A plant climbing
    or scrambling on some
    other support. Such a
    plant may support itself
    by tendrils, or aerial
    roots as in the figure.
    Fig. 183.

AERIAL ROOTS
Fig. 183.

66

10. Tree. A woody plant of considerable stature at maturity,
with one or few main trunks.
This term is often loosely used
and although hard to define is
a fairly well understood concept. Fig. 184.

TREE
Fig. 184.

11. Shrub. A woody plant smaller at
maturity than a tree and usually with
several basal stems. Fig. 185.

SHRUB
Fig. 185.

12. Parasite. A plant growing upon and obtaining
nourishment from another organism, usually lacking green chlorophyll.

13. Saprophyte. A plant that obtains its food from
dead organic material instead of manufacturing
it through the more usual process of photosynthesis. Such a plant is commonly light green
in color or may be lacking green chlorophyll
entirely.

14. Family. A group of related genera.

15. Genus. A group of related species.

16. Species. This has been variously defined but
it is a term for all the individuals of one
kind - from a practical standpoint to students -
those plants that key to and match the same
specific description as outlined in the manuals.

17. Subspecies. One of the variants of a species,
not distinct enough to warrant a separate
specific name, but different enough to be given
a designation.

18. Variety. Used by many authors with the same
meaning as "subspecies". Used by others with a-
bout the same meaning as "forma". The botanical
"variety" may be much different from the horticultural one.

19. **Forma.** A very minor variant, such as a white-flowered plant among a population of blue-flowered ones. The botanists who use the term "subspecies" for a major variant may use the term "variety" for a minor one. This sounds rather confusing, but the beginning student merely has to follow the usage of the manual he is employing.

TEST FOR GENERAL UNDERSTANDING OF PLANTS.

The following outline will give you a chance to check up on your ability to properly diagnose a plant, the first requisite in identifying. Try to answer the 25 questions without consulting a glossary, then if at all possible have your answers checked by an expert. A high score indicates that you have the essential terms in mind so that identification should be reasonably rapid. Several extra pages of this test are included so you can check yourself on more than one plant, or the outline can be used as a formal test in a class.

Write the word that answers the question in the blank space before the number.

Words underlined are to be used in these answers.

Be sure your specimen is not abnormal or badly shattered. For number of parts give the average of several determinations.

_____ 1. Is the plant annual or perennial?

_____ 2. Are rhizomes present or absent?

_____ 3. Name type of inflorescence.

_____ 4. How many sepals?

_____ 5. How many petals?

_____ 6. How many stamens?

_____ 7. How many pistils?

_____ 8. How many carpels to each pistil?

_____ 9. How many locules to each ovary?

_____ 10. Are ovules one, two, several or many to each cell?

_____ 11. Is placentation axile, parietal, basal or free central?

_____ 12. Are stamens opposite or alternate to petals? (or both or neither?)

_____ 13. How many styles to each ovary?

_____ 14. How many stigmas or stigma lobes to each ovary?

_____ 15. Is the flower regular or irregular?

_____ 16. Are the petals separate or united?

_____ 17. Is the flower epigynous, perigynous or hypogynous?

_____ 18. Is the ovary superior or inferior?

_____ 19. Is the stem leafy or scapose?

_____ 20. Are leaves opposite, alternate, whorled, radical or basal?

_____ 21. Are bracts present? (yes or no).

_____ 22. Are the leaves simple or compound? (If compound what special type?)

_____ 23. What term best describes the leaf shape (or leaflet on a compound leaf)?

_____ 24. What term best describes the leaf margin (or leaflet)?

_____ 25. What term best describes the leaf surface (usually lower side)?

Write the word that answers the question in the
blank space before the number

Words underlined are to be used in these
answers.

Be sure your specimen is not abnormal or badly
shattered. For number of parts give the average of
several determinations.

_____ 1. Is the plant annual or perennial?

_____ 2. Are rhizomes present or absent?

_____ 3. Name type of inflorescence.

_____ 4. How many sepals?

_____ 5. How many petals?

_____ 6. How many stamens?

_____ 7. How many pistils?

_____ 8. How many carpels to each pistil?

_____ 9. How many locules to each ovary?

_____ 10. Are ovules one, two, several or many
to each cell?

_____ 11. Is placentation axile, parietal,
basal or free central?

_____ 12. Are stamens opposite or alternate to
petals? (or both or neither?)

_____ 13. How many styles to each ovary?

_____ 14. How many stigmas or stigma lobes to
each ovary?

_____ 15. Is the flower regular or irregular?

_____ 16. Are the petals separate or united?

_____ 17. Is the flower epigynous, perigynous
or hypogynous?

69b

_____ 18. Is the ovary superior or inferior?

_____ 19. Is the stem leafy or scapose?

_____ 20. Are leaves opposite, alternate, whorled, radical or basal?

_____ 21. Are bracts present? (yes or no).

_____ 22. Are the leaves simple or compound? (If compound what special type?)

_____ 23. What term best describes the leaf shape (or leaflet on a compound leaf)?

_____ 24. What term best describes the leaf margin (or leaflet)?

_____ 25. What term best describes the leaf surface (usually lower side)?

Write the word that answers the question in the blank space before the number.

Words underlined are to be used in these answers.

Be sure your specimen is not abnormal or badly shattered. For number of parts give the average of several determinations.

_____ 1. Is the plant annual or perennial?

_____ 2. Are rhizomes present or absent?

_____ 3. Name type of inflorescence.

_____ 4. How many sepals?

_____ 5. How many petals?

_____ 6. How many stamens?

_____ 7. How many pistils?

_____ 8. How many carpels to each pistil?

_____ 9. How many locules to each ovary?

_____ 10. Are ovules one, two, several or many to each cell?

_____ 11. Is placentation axile, parietal, basal or free central?

_____ 12. Are stamens opposite or alternate to petals? (or both or neither?)

_____ 13. How many styles to each ovary?

_____ 14. How many stigmas or stigma lobes to each ovary?

_____ 15. Is the flower regular or irregular?

_____ 16. Are the petals separate or united?

_____ 17. Is the flower epigynous, perigynous or hypogynous?

69c

_____ 18. Is the ovary <u>superior</u> or <u>inferior</u>?

_____ 19. Is the stem <u>leafy</u> or <u>scapose</u>?

_____ 20. Are leaves <u>opposite</u>, <u>alternate</u>, <u>whorled</u>, <u>radical</u> or <u>basal</u>?

_____ 21. Are bracts present? (<u>yes</u> or <u>no</u>).

_____ 22. Are the leaves <u>simple</u> or <u>compound</u>? (If compound what special type?)

_____ 23. What term best describes the leaf shape (or leaflet on a compound leaf)?

_____ 24. What term best describes the leaf margin (or leaflet)?

_____ 25. What term best describes the leaf surface (usually lower side)?

70c

Write the word that answers the question in the blank space before the number.

Words underlined are to be used in these answers.

Be sure your specimen is not abnormal or badly shattered. For number of parts give the average of several determinations.

_____ 1. Is the plant annual or perennial?

_____ 2. Are rhizomes present or absent?

_____ 3. Name type of inflorescence.

_____ 4. How many sepals?

_____ 5. How many petals?

_____ 6. How many stamens?

_____ 7. How many pistils?

_____ 8. How many carpels to each pistil?

_____ 9. How many locules to each ovary?

_____ 10. Are ovules one, two, several or many to each cell?

_____ 11. Is placentation axile, parietal, basal or free central?

_____ 12. Are stamens opposite or alternate to petals? (or both or neither?)

_____ 13. How many styles to each ovary?

_____ 14. How many stigmas or stigma lobes to each ovary?

_____ 15. Is the flower regular or irregular?

_____ 16. Are the petals separate or united?

_____ 17. Is the flower epigynous, perigynous or hypogynous?

_____ 18. Is the ovary superior or inferior?

_____ 19. Is the stem leafy or scapose?

_____ 20. Are leaves opposite, alternate, whorled, radical or basal?

_____ 21. Are bracts present? (yes or no).

_____ 22. Are the leaves simple or compound? (If compound what special type?)

_____ 23. What term best describes the leaf shape (or leaflet on a compound leaf)?

_____ 24. What term best describes the leaf margin (or leaflet)?

_____ 25. What term best describes the leaf surface (usually lower side)?

Chapter XI

FRUITS AND SEEDS

DEFINITIONS.

Fruit.

The fruit is the ripened ovary and any other structure that is closely associated with it.

Seed.

The seed is the matured ovule, containing the small plant (embryo) with a food supply to initiate its development.

Misconceptions.

Many actual fruits are known as "seeds" to the gardner and farmer. The kernel of corn, wheat, or oats, the so-called "seed" of the sunflower, carrot or parsnip is in reality a fruit containing one or two seeds. To many people a "fruit" implies a fleshy structure but this is not necessarily so.

USE OF FRUITS IN IDENTIFICATION.

Differences in fruit types may be used to construct categories in the generic or specific keys. This occurs in the mustard (Cruciferae) and parsley (Umbelliferae) families, as well as in others such as the rose (Rosaceae), legume (Leguminosae) and buttercup (Ranunculaceae) families.

This not only necessitates a clear understanding of fruit types and terms but often creates an additional problem. Flower characters are always used, at least in identifying the plant to the family but flowers and the necessary fruit may not occur together. The thing to do in such a case is to collect a plant in flower, note its floral characters, even saving a specimen if at all possible, then collect a plant later on in fruiting condition. Often an ideal situation occurs and a plant may bear both flowers and fruit at the same time. More commonly still, when several individual plants are examined, some may be in flower and others in fruit. Sometimes the old fruit of the preceding year may remain on the plant or on the ground beneath the plant to help out in this respect.

TERMS NEEDED TO UNDERSTAND THE FRUIT KEY.

Before attempting to diagnose a fruit using the key following this unit it will be necessary to understand a few terms.

1. **Pericarp.** The ripened wall of the matured ovary in the fruit is called a pericarp. Sometimes three layers can be distinguished, the outer exocarp, the middle mesocarp and the inner endocarp. (See Fig. 188 under "drupe".)

2. **Fleshy.** This means succulent and watery at maturity like an apple, cherry, raspberry or tomato.

3. **Dry.** Dry at maturity. For example a bean pod is fleshy and edible when young but becomes dry upon ripening.

4. **Dehiscent.** A fruit that opens naturally to release the enclosed seed or seeds.

5. **Suture.** A suture is the line of dehiscence. (See Fig. 186.)

6. **Septum.** A partition between the cells of an ovary or fruit. (See Fig. 186.)

7. **Valve.** One of the segments of a dehiscent fruit after opening. The right-hand drawing shows a cross-section of the fruit before the valves have separated widely. Fig. 186.

VALVES OF DEHISCENT FRUIT

SEPTUM VALVE LOCULE SUTURE PLACENTA

Fig. 186.

8. **Indehiscent.** A fruit that does not open to release the seed or seeds. Fleshy fruits are practically always indehiscent as are most dry one-seeded fruits. The seed eventually may germinate and force its way through the walls of the fruit unless these have already decayed away.

9. **Locule (cell).** One of the compartments of an ovary or fruit. (See Fig. 186 under "valve".)

10. **Carpel.** One of the individual parts of a compound ovary, theoretically that part formed from one sporophyll in its evolutionary development. The rule is to count the number of locules (cells), placentae, styles and stigma lobes. The highest number will be the number of carpels. This whole situation is discussed and figured at the end of Chapter IV. In the 3 figures above, the center one would have 1 carpel if the ovary had but one cell and one placenta. The other two figures show ovaries or fruits in cross-section, with three carpels indicated for each. Fig. 187.

CARPELS

Fig. 187.

Key to the Common Fruits

1. Fruit fleshy

    2. Pistil one, simple, one-seeded, endocarp stony------------Drupe (Plum) (1.)

    2. Pistils either more than one, or if one with more than one carpel and usually many seeded, endocarp not stony

        3. Pistils more than one, from the same flower or from more than one flower

            4. Pistils of one flower forming individual fruit

                5. Receptacle very fleshy, pistils achene-like, dry---Accessory (Strawberry) (2.)

                5. Receptacle not very fleshy, pistils drupe-like, fleshy-Aggregate (Raspberry) (3.)

            4. Pistils from more than one flower forming one individual fruit

                6. Bulk of fruit from a hypanthium, which encloses many pistils-------Syconium (Fig) (4.)

                6. Bulk of fruit from many fleshy, superior pistils densely clustered-Multiple (Mulberry)(5.)

        3. Pistil one to a fruit, compound

            7. Ovary superior, receptacle not forming part of fruit

                8. Covering of fruit thin, not leathery------Berry (Tomato) (6.)

                8. Covering of fruit thick and leathery-Hesperidium (Orange)(7.)

7. Ovary inferior, receptacle (or calyx tube) forming part of fruit

    9. Receptacle forming only a tough, hard, outer rind--------Pepo (Watermelon) (8.)

    9. Receptacle fleshy, thick, forming the bulk of the fruit------Pome (Apple) (9.)

1. Fruit dry at maturity, not fleshy

    10. Indehiscent, the seeds not falling out of fruit, usually one-seeded (2-seeded in (Schizocarps and some Samaras)

        11. Fruit of 2 or more carpels that separate at maturity leaving the common axis between them--
            Schizocarp (Carrot) (10.)

        11. Only one carpel, or if two (as in some Samaras) not leaving an axis between when they separate

            12. Fruit winged-
                Samara (Maple, Ash) (11.)

            12. F uit not winged

                13. Wall tough and hard-
                    Nut (Acorn, Walnut) (12.)
                  (A small nut-like fruit is a nutlet.)

                13. Wall not especially hard and tough

                    14. Seed attached to ovary wall at only one point-
                    Achene (Sunflower)(13.)

                    14. Seed attached to ovary wall at all points-
                    Caryopsis (Corn, Wheat) (14.)

10. Dehiscent, the seeds commonly many

15. Only one line of dehiscence, ovary of one carpel----------------Follicle (Milkweed) (15.)

15. Two or more lines of dehiscence, ovary of one or more than one carpel

   16. Fruit one-celled, one carpel present

      17. Pod constricted between the seeds, tending to break into one-seeded segments--Loment (Beggar's Lice)(16.)

      17. Pod not especially constricted, not breaking up---Legume (Pea, Bean)(17.)

   16. Fruit more than one-celled (partition thin and sometimes hard to see in a silique and silicle), or if one-celled, with 2 or more carpels present

      18. The two carpels pulling away leaving a thin central septum

         19. Fruit short and broad Silicle (Pepper grass) (18.)

         19. Fruit long and narrow Silique (Mustard) (19.)

      18. Carpels as they pull apart leaving no partition in the center (or opening by pores or lids at apex), often over two carpels present- Capsule (Lily) (20.)

         There are 4 types of capsules:- Opening by pores- Poricidal (Poppy) (20A.)

         Opening along septa Septicidal (Yucca) (20B.)

         Opening along middle of locule Loculicidal (Iris) (20C.)

         Opening by a lid, along a circular horizontal line--Circumscissile or a pyxis (Purslane, Plantain) (20D.)

DEFINITIONS AND DRAWINGS OF THE FRUITS IN THE KEY.

1. **Drupe.** A fleshy indehiscent fruit, one-seeded, with the endocarp stony. Fig. 188.

DRUPE

EXOCARP
MESOCARP
ENDOCARP
SEED

Fig. 188.

2. **Accessory.** A fleshy fruit like a strawberry, made up of a succulent receptacle covered with several to many pistils, each forming a dry achene-like fruit. Sometimes not distinguished from **aggregate**. Fig. 189.

ACCESSORY FRUIT

FLESHY RECEPTACLE
ACHENES

Fig. 189.

3. **Aggregate.** A fruit with the receptacle not especially fleshy, with several to many pistils, these each becoming fleshy and drupe-like. The blackberry and raspberry are examples. In the lefthand drawing the cluster of drupes has been removed leaving the naked receptacle, as occurs in the raspberry. Fig. 190.

AGGREGATE FRUIT

CLUSTER OF DRUPES
RECEPTACLE

Fig. 190.

4. **Syconium.** A fruit made up of a fleshy hollow receptacle bearing inside many small separate flowers, each of which may produce a seed-like nutlet. A Fig is a good example. In the drawing the fruit is shown in longitudinal section. Fig. 191.

SYCONIUM

OVARY
RECEPTACLE
"HYPANTHIUM"

Fig. 191.

5. **Multiple.** A fleshy fruit formed from
    several to many separate flowers.
    These flowers have superior ovaries
    which may become fleshy but other
    parts of the unit may also be suc-
    culent. The classic example is borne
    on the mulberry plant. Such a fruit
    may resemble an aggregate fruit but
    is not formed from one flower.
    Fig. 192.

MULTIPLE FRUIT

Fig. 192.

6. **Berry.** A fleshy fruit formed from
    one compound ovary containing few to
    many seeds. This fruit appears in
    the key as formed from a superior
    ovary, however, the term is often
    loosely used to include pulpy fruits
    formed from an inferior ovary but
    not resembling a pepo or pome.
    Fig. 193.

THIN SKIN

SEED

FLESHY

BERRY

Fig. 193.

7. **Hesperidium.** This is a berry-like fruit with a
    thick leathery covering. An orange is a good ex-
    ample. Fig. 194.

8. **Pepo.** A fleshy fruit formed from a compound in-
    ferior ovary, the outer wall becoming rather
    hard and tough. watermelon and cucumber have
    this type of fruit. Fig. 195.

9. **Pome.** A fleshy fruit formed from an inferior
    compound ovary, the receptacle (or calyx tube)
    fleshy and thick. The apple is a pome.
    Fig. 196.

HESPERIDIUM
Fig. 194.

PEPO
Fig. 195.

POME
Fig. 196.

10. Schizocarp. A dry indehiscent fruit made up of
2 or more 1-seeded carpels
that separate at maturity
leaving a common axis be-
tween (the carpophore).
Sometimes each segment is
called a "mericarp". The
drawing to the left shows a
cross-section of such a
fruit. Some manuals may
call this fruit a cremo-
carp. Fig. 197.

SCHIZOCARP

Fig. 197.

11. Samara. A dry indehiscent
winged fruit like those on
a maple (double samara) or
ash (single). Fig. 198.

Fig. 198.

12. Nut. A dry, indehiscent one-seeded fruit with
a hard coat. Often rather loosely used.

13. Achene. A dry indehiscent one-
seeded fruit, the seed connected
to the pericarp at only one point.
The sunflower has achenes. In the
figure the seed is shown as if
shrunken away from the pericarp.
Fig. 199.

ACHENE

Fig. 199.

14. Caryopsis (grain). A dry
indehiscent one-seeded
fruit, the seed connected
to the pericarp at all
points. The corn kernel
is a caryopsis. Fig. 200.

PERICARP

EMBRYO

CARYOPSIS

Fig. 200.

15. **Follicle.** A dry one-celled, one-carpellate fruit splitting down one side only, as in the milkweed. Fig. 201.

FOLLICLE
Fig. 201.

16. **Loment.** A dry one-celled, one-carpellate fruit constricted between the seeds. Otherwise like the more common <u>legume</u>. Fig. 202.

LOMENT
Fig. 202.

17. **Legume.** A dry one-celled, one-carpellate fruit splitting down two sides. Often called a "pod", a loosely used term. Fig. 203.

LEGUME
Fig. 203.

18. **Silicle.** A dry two-celled dehiscent fruit, each half pulling away at maturity leaving a thin central septum. A silicle is usually not more than twice as long as wide. The righthand drawing shows the 2 valves pulled away from the septum and pushed to the sides. Fig. 204.

SILICLE
Fig. 204.

19. **Silique.** A dry two-celled dehiscent fruit each half pulling away at maturity leaving a thin central septum. The length is more than twice the width. Fig. 205.

SILIQUE
Fig. 205.

80

20. Capsule. A dry dehiscent fruit made up of more than one carpel. It may be one-celled with one line of dehiscence but the placentae would be more than one. This is a very common type of fruit.

A. Poricidal capsule. One that opens by means of pores, as in a poppy. Fig. 206.

B. Septicidal capsule. One that opens along the septa by splitting it. Fig. 207.

C. Loculicidal capsule. One that opens along the middle of the locule. Fig. 208.

PORICIDAL CAPSULE
Fig. 206.

SEPTICIDAL CAPSULE
Fig. 207.

LOCULICIDAL CAPSULE
Fig. 208.

D. Circumscissile capsule (pyxis). One that opens by a lid along a circular horizontal line. Fig. 209.

CIRCUMSCISSILE CAPSULE
Fig. 209.

SEEDS.

Mature seeds are usually not yet present on a plant that bears the flowers necessary for identification. However, in some genera like Mentzelia and Epilobium seed characters may actually be used as categories in the key. In such cases seeds may be obtained from more mature individuals or even from fruits of the preceding year. The various Seed Testing Laboratories have developed a technique whereby they can identify the seeds and small fruits of common weeds when they come in as a contaminate in crop seeds, but here the actual possibilities are limited of course.

VARIATIONS OF SEEDS.

Seeds vary in different ways, the commonest ones listed below.

1. Size. The coconut has a very large seed, the orchid a very small one.

2. Hairs. Some seeds bear hairs such as in Epilob-ium (fireweed) and Asclepias (milkweed), these function in aiding the distribution of these objects by the wind.

3. Wings. Some seeds as well as some fruits have wings, like those borne by some species of Mentzelia (stickleaf); these may be used in classification.

4. Shape. The typical shape is round or oval but seeds may vary widely in this respect.

5. Color. Seeds may vary strikingly in color but sometimes the difference may be so subtle that it can be perceived only by trained eyes like those of an expert seed analyst. An example of a conspicuous color is found in a species of Sophora (coral bean) which has a bright scarlet seed.

6. Surface markings. Seeds may have very elaborate and striking designs and surface sculpturings, these often taking the form of raised or indented tracery.

7. Hilum and raphe. The scar where the seed broke away from the fruit (hilum) and the ridge that appears adjacent to it (raphe) often vary in shape, prominence, position, etc. Fig. 210.

TYPICAL SEED

Fig. 210.

8. Embryo. The position, size, shape and number of the cotyledons is sometimes used in families like the Chenopodiaceae (Goosefoot family). This means that mature seeds and fruit are necessary in order to secure a positive check on this character, which means a rather close study under a dissecting microscope or good hand lens.

Chapter XII

USE OF KEYS IN PLANT IDENTIFICATION

WHY KEYS ARE NECESSARY.

Keys provide a convenient short cut method of de-
termining plants by outlining and grouping related
types. There is a particular "knack" in using keys,
gained partly by certain native ability in weighing
evidence in order to arrive at a correct decision,
but obtained mostly by constant practice and experience. If the student has in mind a good concept as
to the meaning of the common descriptive terms and a
correct understanding of the characters of the plant
under consideration, then identifying it through the
key should not be so difficult.
It is suggested that this chapter be studied carefully only after the student has had at least some
practice in identification.

TYPES OF KEYS.

1. Synoptical. This key runs through the descriptions as headings. Often more than one choice
   is presented and usually more than one species
   (in specific key) is listed under the last head-
   ing. This involves reading over several specific
   descriptions as the final step. Only the older
   manuals use this type of key, consequently no example is given here.

2. Bracket. In this key the two choices always
   stand together. An example would be:

1. Flowers red --------------------------------------- 2

1. Flowers blue-------------------------------------- 5

   2. Leaves simple----------------------------- 3

   2. Leaves compound-------------------------- 4

3. Petals 4-------------------------Species no. 1

3. Petals 5-------------------------Species no. 2

   4. Leaflets 5--------------------Species no. 3

   4. Leaflets 9-11----------------Species no. 4

5. Flowers sessile---------------------Species no. 5

5. Flowers pedicelled-----------------------------6

    6. Inflorescence a raceme---------Species no. 6

    6. Inflorescence a panicle--------Species no. 7

    Some authors do not even indent every other pair of choices. In any case the bracket key saves space and is easier to set up for printing. However, it does not outline the group in as definite a manner as the Indented Key and is more difficult to use if it is necessary to "try" both categories (See Hints in Using Keys, number 3).

3. Indented Key. Here the group is outlined and better organized as each new pair of choices is set off by an indentation. In the example given the pairs have a like number to aid in locating the contrasting choice. This is particularly useful in a long key where the other member of the pair may be several pages distant. When no numbers are used you find the opposite choice by similarity in indentation and also by comparing the context which should be in contrast in the two categories. The key given below is for the same plants that were treated in the Bracket Key.

1. Flowers red

    2. Leaves simple

        3. Petals 4--------------------Species no. 1

        3. Petals 5--------------------Species no. 2

    2. Leaves compound

        4. Leaflets 5----------------Species no. 3

        4. Leaflets 9-11--------------Species no. 4

1. Flowers blue

    5. Flowers sessile----------------Species no. 5

    5. Flowers pedicelled

6.   Inflorescence a raceme-----Species no. 6

6.   Inflorescence a panicle----Species no. 7

Notice that all the red flowers fall together
making a more logical outline of the group. The
majority of the modern manuals use this type of key.
It does waste some space to the left of the page
and is a typist's nightmare but most botanists prefer to use such a key over the Bracket type.

DIFFICULTIES IN USING KEYS.

Like the human beings who create them, botanical
keys are not perfect. Listed below are some of the
difficulties you can expect to encounter in using
keys. Do not be too ready to find fault with the
author of your treatment, at least until you are certain you yourself have not made a blunder. An excellent way to gain sympathy for the creator of your
keys is to try your own hand at making one. Some
suggestions for handling some of these difficulties
will be given later on in this chapter.

1.   The key may use characters not present on your
     specimen. For example the generic key to the
     family Ranunculaceae (Buttercup Family) is usual-
     ly based on the type of fruit, but floral char-
     acters are necessary to key the plant to the
     family. If your plant does not have both flowers
     and fruit you have a problem.

2.   The key is set up for the average plant. Your
     specimen may be abnormal in some way. The remedy
     is to select one or more average plants and avoid
     the unusual or freakish specimens.

3.   In some keys the author may ring in more than 2
     choices. This is especially disconcerting if the
     third choice happens to fall on a different page.
     However, few if any of the recently printed man-
     uals have this fault.

4.   The exact meaning of some terms may vary with the
     different manuals used. Certain terms like
     caespitose, canescent, elliptic, membranous,
     decumbent and pubescent are loosely used by some
     botanists. If you use one manual only, this
     problem should not arise.

5. The meanings of some terms vary somewhat when used
    for different groups. "Plants tall" may mean a
    few centimeters when used with Stellaria
    (Chickweed) or it may mean several meters tall
    when used with Betula (Birch tree). Similarly
    the size of a "large flowered" buttercup would
    give you a "small flowered" rose. The remedy of
    course would be for your manual to use concrete
    measurements with the understanding that unusual
    specimens may fall above or below the figure
    given.

6. The characters given in the first category of the
    pair may not be all contrasted in the second.
    This seems to be a very common fault in key mak-
    ing where secondary characters are stated in one
    place and ignored in the other. For example, you
    may read "Flowers white; plants annual" as con-
    trasted to "Flowers yellow". Very often the dur-
    ation habit of the yellow flowered plants can be
    puzzled out by reading further in the key.

7. Keys are in fine print and it is easy to overlook
    a line entirely and miss an important step. The
    remedy is to take your time in using a key.

8. The key may be actually ambiguous or faulty in
    places due to an out-and-out mistake of the
    author. This is unfortunate because as a student
    you have to trust your key. A teacher in the
    laboratory can help you over such places. If you
    are on your own all you can do is to check your
    plant again, perhaps try other parts of the key,
    then if you always come back to the same place
    you might suspect an error in the treatment. For
    example, if you always arrive at 2 choices,
    "Flowers red" as opposed to "Flowers white" with
    a yellow flowered plant, it may be that the
    writer of the key inadvertently left off the "or
    yellow" and the last choice should have read,
    "Flowers white or yellow". You can check on this
    by trial.

        Sometimes the "exception" is not properly
    provided for, especially in a manual treating
    large numbers of plants. For example, in a blue-
    flowered genus one species may have white
    flowers. This may be overlooked and the generic
    key may put the genus under "flowers blue" only.

The particular "knack" in using keys in a large part is in being able to sense when the key is faulty or misleading. This is easier to do after you have had considerable experience following one manual.

9. The plant you are trying to identify may not be included in the key. You may have a weedy species that has come in since the book was written and may even have become locally abundant. Or your plant may be a rare one whose exact limits were not understood at the time the manual was written. When you come to suspect that this is the case the remedy is to try to key out the plant in manuals treating the plants of adjacent areas or send a specimen to some expert botanist for checking.

HINTS ON USING KEYS.

The way to attain proficiency in keying plants is to practice continuously. Even when the work of the day occupies your daylight hours there will usually be a few minutes in the evening when you can check over some of the plants picked up during the day. It is as easy to become "rusty" in identifying plants as it is in almost any kind of skill. An experienced botanist uses several "tricks" to help him get around certain difficulties in a key. Some of these are listed below.

1. Look the whole plant over in a general way before you start keying it. The alternative would be to deal with each character as it appears in the key.

2. Check yourself at every possible step with the descriptions. For example, when you arrive at a family in the key take time to read over the family description before proceeding. This may save you a lot of back tracking later on.

3. Run the plant both ways in doubtful cases. In the incorrect way the key usually begins to read all wrong. For example, you may meet a place where your only 2 choices are "Flowers red", as opposed to "Flowers yellow". If your plant has blue flowers you might conclude you have tried the wrong road. Or you may run the plant down to

87

a certain species and upon consulting the specific description find that it just will not fit. But on trying the correct path, the key begins to read right and the descriptions fit better.

In a long key several of these alternate "trials" can be made. Very often a positive identification can be secured with this method when for one reason or another it is impossible to make positive choices at several places in the key.

4. If your manual has pictures or drawings of the species, use them to check your identification. It is seldom possible to identify a plant by thumbing through these figures since the specific differences may be based on characters that cannot be shown in a drawing. Remember a drawing is a static thing but the individuals constituting a species are not. A good description is far superior to a drawing to illustrate this range of variability. For that reason most manuals do not try to illustrate each species. Pictures ought to illustrate the diagnostic visual characters. An excellent way to use them is to check the visual characters used in the key by referring to pictured examples under each category. Remember that your plant can actually look more like the figure of species number one when it may actually be species number two! The key and description should have the final word on the subject.

5. Learn to weigh and evaluate the important characters in cases of doubt. Usually the floral structures have more importance than vegetative ones. For example, if your plant has the correct flower length for one species but fits better under another for height of plant you would do much better in giving the greater weight to the floral character.

6. Use your knowledge of the group to help. This comes only with experience. An experienced worker is constantly reasoning something like this, "My plant cannot be this species because I am familiar with it and it is much different, therefore I must take the other road in the key."

But beware of preconceived notions that may be wrong. If the plant will not key out, start anew and check every character — even major ones!

88

7. Check your final determination by reference to the recorded habitat. The habitat is the local condition under which a plant grows. If a description ends by saying "plants of wet soil, borders of ponds and marshes", and your plant came from a dry hilltop, you are justified in suspecting your identification. This must be done with caution as your manual may give incomplete or even faulty information on the matter.

8. Check your identification by reference to the recorded locality. If your manual excludes your state for the species, perhaps even by the interval of several states, you have a right to suspect your identification. Again this must be done with caution especially with weedy plants. Even with native plants new information is constantly accumulating concerning this distribution.

9. Read all the supplemental characters, not just the first one. But do not fix on a second or third minor one and ignore the more important first one (unless this is unavoidable).

10. Always read both contrasting statements before you decide. The first one may sound so good that the second choice may be ignored. But get both sides of the picture; the second category, by contrast, may actually help to explain the first one.

11. Experience teaches you when you can assume a minor error in the key or description. For example, if the corolla length is listed as "2 to 5 mm. long" and yours runs 5.5 to 6 mm. it may be wise to "give in" on the matter if the plant fits everywhere else. This must be done with caution as you may be in the wrong place entirely!

12. In measuring an object such as the length of a leaf of a flower part, always select a large one. Pick one somewhat larger than the average but not an abnormal one. Apparently the manuals and floras expect you to do that.

Chapter XIII

COLLECTING AND PRESSING PLANTS

VALUES OF COLLECTING AND PRESSING PLANTS.

1. One of the very best ways to learn plants is to
   collect and press them. Otherwise when many
   plants are identified the later ones tend to
   crowd out the earlier ones in your mind. But if
   you save a specimen you can refer to it constantly. Each time you change blotters as explained
   below, write out a label or fix the plant to the
   sheet, you get a chance to see the specimen.

   The plant looks different in the field as it
   grows but consulting your specimen is an excellent way to recall to memory its appearance. If
   you have pressed the plant yourself you know
   what happens in the process. Many botanists can
   look at their specimens and recall to mind the
   exact appearance of almost every one as it looked
   when collected. One such botanist who had collected thousands of specimens over a period of 50
   years claimed that by looking at the pressed
   plants he was able to remember the exact details
   of every collection.

2. Collecting and pressing allows for securing large
   numbers of plants when the opportunity occurs,
   and identifying them later when more time is
   available. Many botanists spend all summer collecting specimens during daylight hours, putting
   them in presses during the evenings, then identifying and mounting them during the winter.
   With such a procedure it is surprising how many
   plants can be dealt with in a season.

3. By collecting the plant you have an opportunity
   of checking up on your identification by sub-
   mitting the specimen to an authority. If possible collect duplicate material and keep one
   specimen for yourself. Almost any expert is
   willing to check material for you if your plants
   are well collected, well pressed and have complete and dependable data attached. His payment

is a good specimen of the plant for his collection.

4. A set of named specimens will often prove useful
    to aid in checking the identity of later collections by comparison. It is seldom possible
    to actually identify a plant from the beginning
    by leafing over a collection since so many
    species are involved. But it does allow for
    checking your determination or helping decide between possibilities. Be certain your pressed
    plant is correctly named and remember that two
    individuals of a species may not look exactly
    alike. The comparison should be made on the
    basis of the important diagnostic characters
    used in the group concerned. It is possible
    that the individual plant you are checking may
    actually resemble more closely in general appearance a specimen of the wrong species than it
    does of the correct one!

5. A collection of plant specimens provides an authentic record of the species of an area.
    Every printed list of plants ought to be backed
    up in this concrete fashion. If anyone doubts
    your identification of a particular plant you
    can always refer him to your specimen.

GENERAL DIRECTIONS FOR COLLECTING PLANTS.

1. Select an average plant or collect several specimens showing the range of variation. Remember
    that your specimen is to be representative of
    the species in that area. There is a temptation
    to collect "freaks" or "off color" plants as
    oddities but if you do so, be sure to state the
    situation clearly on the label

2. Collect the plant in flower if possible. In
    special groups where rather mature fruit is
    necessary, like the Cruciferae (mustard family)
    or Umbelliferae (carrot family) look around and
    try to find a plant with both flowers and fruit
    present. Sometimes you may find one plant in
    flower and another in fruit and the two can be
    mounted together.

3. Collect all the plant when possible, including the underground parts, especially if these are unusual in some way (such as bulbs, corms, rhizomes, etc.). In any case collect enough to give a clue as to the annual or perennial habit of a herbaceous plant. The roots of woody plants are seldom collected, however.

A large plant can be bent or folded to fit your equipment. With a very large plant certain representative portions can be selected; these parts will usually be the flowers and leaves. Avoid selecting very small plants; they may fit your mounting sheet but may not be representative of the species.

4. Place the plant at once in the press, vasculum or collecting can. This is particularly important in arid regions. A really good specimen is impossible to make from a wilted plant.

5. Keep accurate information about each plant; better use a field notebook rather than to depend on memory alone. All or most of this data will appear on the label so it must be accurate. An inaccurate or misplaced label can cause trouble and confusion for years and even centuries. The information you may need for your label is listed below.

(1.) Absolutely necessary information.

A. The habitat or local conditions under which a plant grows. In mountainous areas the altitude where the collection was made is important.

B. The locality, preferably by reference to a town, county and state. Such information should allow someone else to find the approximate area if they wish. Very local names like "Happy Hollow" or "Smith's Ranch", should not be used, at least alone. By referring to a county and town anyone consulting your specimen can figure out the exact locality from a map. Even when the town has ceased to exist, it will still be recorded on older maps.

C. The day, month and year of collection.

D. The name of the collector.

(2.) Very desirable information.

    A. Color of the flowers. This may be partly or completely obscured in the pressing.

    B. Height of the plant if only a portion is collected. This is particularly important in dealing with woody plants such as shrubs and trees. The type of branching may be worth recording especially if it is unusual. For example, you may not be able to tell from a pressed specimen whether the stem was decumbent or ascending.

    C. Technical information you need to identify plants in that group but which does not show up well on pressed material. For example, in the genus Castilleja (paint brushes) one may need to know if the calyx is cut deeper above or below in order to key out the species. By recording this information you later save yourself and others the bother of detaching and soaking up a flower.

(3.) Special information you may need yourself.

    This may be almost anything but may include some of the following.

    A. Ecological information such as plant formation, soil type, etc.

    B. Economic importance such as grazing value, importance as a weed, use in medicine, etc.

    C. Relative abundance in the locality.

    D. Field variations observed.

    E. Insect visitors to the plant.

    F. A photograph of the plant to be pasted on the mounting sheet along with the label.

EQUIPMENT FOR COLLECTING PLANTS.

These vary with the individual. Every experienced collector has certain pet tools and gad-
gets suited to his particular needs or tempera-
ment. The following list is almost essential.

1. Digging tool. This may be variable but should
be painted some bright color to aid in locating
it if it is forgotten. In the photograph A.
is a hand pick, B. is a small trowel-like digger
while C. is a strong hunting knife. If possible
try them all before selecting one. Better yet
construct for yourself the ideal one! Fig. 211.

Fig. 211.

2. Sharp knife. This is to cut off parts such as
twigs of woody plants. A pocket knife does very
well.

Note: Recently many collectors have been using
plastic bags of varying sizes to store fresh
plants in the field. Such containers are handy
to carry, light in weight and prevent the material from drying out. Many workers use numerous
small bags.

94

3. Container. This is for storing the plants until they can be put away in the presses. The object is to prevent undue wilting. On cold days plants may be kept all day in excellent condition in a vasculum. A. is a hand press, B. is a vasculum, C. is a lard can and D. is an ordinary plant press. Fig. 212.

Fig. 212.

      The vasculum can be carried around, the lard can may be used as a central storehouse. Many botanists do not use any collecting can at all but place the plant at once in a temporary press called a hand press (Fig. 212A.). This usually consists of many single sheets of paper within a stiff cover like wallboard, the whole supported by straps attached to a handle for convenience in carrying.

4. Conveyance. Automobile, train, horse, bicycle, boat or walking. The wide use of the automobile has resulted in a great deal of roadside collecting. The most interesting areas for finding unusual plants often lie away from the highways.

SOURCES FOR COLLECTING EQUIPMENT.

Many of the implements mentioned above can be found at your local stores. A vasculum can be constructed by your local tinsmith. A few supply houses are given below in case you wish to purchase these items.

1. General Biological Supply House, 8200 South Hoyne Avenue, Chicago, Illinois.

2. Wards Natural Science Establishment Inc., 3000 Ridge Road East, Rochester 9, New York.

DIRECTIONS FOR PRESSING PLANTS.

1. Give each plant a number, these numbers running in consecutive order through the lifetime of the collector. This number corresponds to that used in the Field Notebook.

2. Place the plant in a once-folded paper cover approximately $16\frac{1}{2}$ x $11\frac{1}{2}$ inches in size. An ordinary newspaper sheet will make this folder, in addition it may provide someone with interesting reading 40 or 50 years later! The number of the plant is placed on the paper folder and this stays with the specimen throughout the process.

3. Arrange the plant so that the floral parts are well displayed. It may be necessary to bend the stem once or more times and remove some leaves.

4. Place this folder with its specimen between thick blotters of about the same size (18 x 12 inches works very well). If blotters are not available you can use all or part of a folded newspaper which acts as a blotter. A board is placed on the pile and a weight is placed on top. A flat stone does very well if it weighs about 20 or 30 lbs. A conventional plant press is made up of 2 boards, often latticed, with straps or ropes around them, and this can be readily transported (Fig. 212 D.).

5. Replace these blotters with dry ones as needed. The wet ones can be dried out and used again later. Plants with watery thick parts may dry slowly. A good rule is to change blotters every 24 hours for two or three times, then every 48

hours until the plant has been pressed flat and is perfectly dry. You soon learn by experience how long this period will be. If you are in a hurry or the air is humid and moist, it is necessary to use artificial heat. Corrugated cardboards (or aluminum corrugates sold by supply houses) are inserted among the plant sheets and the press is suspended over a heat source. Of course the heat must not be too intense. Botanists often have a special box constructed that contains a heating unit and a fan at the base.

6. Secure thin cardboard sheets $11\frac{1}{2}$ x $16\frac{1}{2}$ inches in size. Ordinary thin paper does not hold its shape very well but very thick cardboard takes up too much space. These sheets can be secured from a paper supply company or can be ordered from a biological supply house (see list in this chapter).

7. Glue the specimens to this sheet or fasten them with strips of gummed cloth. Many botanists use a tin paste for this purpose but ordinary glue does very well. Recently strips of liquid plastic have been used to hold down the specimen. Gummed paper may become brittle in time as is the case with scotch tape. Often both gluing and stripping are used. The strips are placed in a fashion to prevent the plant from slipping lengthwise out of the fasteners. Leave space at the lower righthand corner for the label.

8. The labels should be about 3 x $4\frac{1}{2}$ inches in size or somewhat smaller. You can have them printed with your name if you wish. Space should be available for the necessary information and anything else of a special nature. These labels are for sale at the biological supply houses.

9. Store the plants so that they are accessible. The usual way is to place the species of a genus in a folded cardboard cover, these genera are arranged by families. Such folders can be stored in cabinets or cases. A constant watch should be kept to prevent damage from insects. These pests may actually breed in the cases and the larvae can soon ruin a collection. Some

botanists fumigate the material periodically
with Hydrocyanic Acid fumes or other insecticides
of similar nature. Paradichlorobenzine flakes
may act as a repellent or spraying at intervals
with a DDT solution may protect the plants. An
insect tight case is of course desirable to keep
out these pests.

Chapter XIV

MANUALS AND FLORAS

A manual or flora has been written for identifying the
plants of every area in the United States. Some of these books
are rather old; others are new and up-to-date in nomenclature
and treatment. Unfortunately many are now out of print and
must be obtained at libraries or from secondhand book dealers,
but fortunately some have recently been reprinted and are
available from such publishers as Dover, Hafner, etc.

Only the most important manuals and floras are listed in
this chapter, and the list is generally limited to those
treating the plants of Canada and the United States. If you
wish to identify plants from other countries, see below and
the next page. For Canada and the United States, a more complete list than noted with the 5 maps is on pp. 100-113. Additional listings have been added at a later date; see the un-
numbered items on the pages facing the first 3 maps (pp. 114-118).

1. Blake, S. F. and Atwood, A. C. Geographical
    Guide to Floras of the World. Part I.
    U. S. D. A. Misc. Pub. 401. 1942.

        This first part deals with Africa,
    Australasia, Insular Floras, North America and
    South America. The second part of this useful
    work will cover Asia and Europe.

2. Lawrence, G. H. M. Taxonomy of the Vascular
    Plants. The MacMillan Company, New York, N. Y.
    1051.

        Chapter XIV deals with the Literature of
    Systematic Botany and gives the more important
    manuals and floras of the various continents
    and islands of the world.

3. Blake, S. F. Guide to Popular Floras of the
    United States and Alaska. U. S. D. A. Biblio-
    graphical Bulletin No. 23. June, 1954.

        Many of the "popular" floras listed are
    based on careful and continuous study of the
    plants of the area covered. They may contain

diagnostic keys very useful in identifying the plants. Often they treat special groups, such as the woody plants of the area, using characters of twig and leaf which allows for the identification of these plants before or after the flowering period.

4. Core, E. L. Plant Taxonomy. Prentice Hall, Inc. 1955.

   Chapter XI deals with the literature of Systematic Botany.

WORLD.

1. Bentham, G. and Hooker, J. D. Genera Plantarum. 3 volumes. London. 1862-1883.

   In Latin. Devoted to the genera of seed plants, grouped under families. No formal keys are given but the major groupings are separated by synoptical devices. No attempt is made of course to provide means for identifying the species.

2. Engler, A. and Prantl, K. Die naturlichen Pflanzenfamilien. 23 volumes. Leipzig. 1887-1915; edition 2, 1924 - Incomplete (1957).

   In German. This treats the families and genera of the world (except the Bacteria). It is well illustrated and carries the classification down to the genera with keys to the major groupings. The second edition promises to be of special value to students of the world flora.

UNITED STATES - SPECIAL GROUPS.

These books treat a particular group of plants over a wide area. In addition monographs and revisions of certain taxonomic groups may be available. These usually treat a particular genus as represented in a certain geographical area. Often this area may be the United States or North America. If you know the genus then these monographs can be used to determine the species. Unfortunately most such treatments are unavailable to the average student, scattered as they are through various periodicals.

100

No attempt is made to list these numerous works here.
The pertinent information from these monographs
eventually becomes incorporated in the manuals and
floras listed later on in this chapter.

1. Grasses

  1. Hitchcock, A. S. Manual of the Grasses of
     the United States. Second edition revised
     by Agnes Chase, U. S. D. A. Misc. Pub. 200.
     Washington, D. C. 1951.

        An illustrated treatment of the family
     Gramineae (Poaceae) as represented in the
     United States. It is based on the huge
     grass collection assembled at the U. S.
     National Herbarium. The species are illus-
     trated and described.

2. Cultivated plants

  1. Bailey, L. H. Manual of Cultivated Plants.
     Edition 2. 1116 pages. The MacMillan Co.,
     New York. 1949.

        The plants commonly grown in the United
     States and Canada are keyed out and describ-
     ed. The general arrangement is similar to
     the manuals with which the student is famil-
     iar. Single citations only are given for
     the scientific names.

  2. Bailey, L. H. The Standard Cyclopedia of
     Horticulture. 6 vols. 1914-1917. (The
     second edition of 1922 was re-issued in 1935
     in 3 volumes.)

        Provides keys to and descriptions of
     the plants commonly cultivated in the United
     States and Canada with information as to
     their culture and use. The first volume con-
     tains a synopsis of the plant kingdom with a
     key to the families and genera. The genera
     are arranged alphabetically throughout the
     rest of the work. The family key is diffi-
     cult for students and the work as a whole is
     bulky and hard to transport. For that reason
     the smaller Bailey's Manual is recommended
     for ordinary use in identifying cultivated
     plants.

3. Rehder, Alfred. Manual of Cultivated Trees and Shrubs. 825 pages. Second edition 1940. MacMillan Co.

This book is on the order of a regular manual with keys and descriptions to the woody plants grown in North America. The keys are based on floral characters. Since most of the common native woody plants have been in cultivation at one time or another, the publication is very useful for identifying the general flora.

3. Trees

1. Sargent, C. S. Manual of the Trees of North America Exclusive of Mexico. Illustrated. Second Edition. Houghton-Mifflin Co., 1922.

Provides keys to families, genera and species. In addition the species are described and illustrated. Really an abridgment of the author's 14 volume set called "The Silva of North Ameria" which is usually unavailable to the average student.

UNITED STATES - GENERAL FLORA.

1. Britton, N. L., et al. North American Flora. Published by the New York Botanical Garden. 1905 - not completed (1957).

Planned in 34 volumes and will include all the native plants of North American from bacteria and algae through the seed plants. The work to date has been done by various specialists of the groups concerned but under a uniform editorial policy. Prior to 1935 the American Code of Nomenclature was followed, since that time the International Rules have been used. If the particular family or genus is recognized by the student and has been treated in this publication to date then the work would be a valuable aid to the student in identification of plants. Usually the complete manuals and floras covering a more limited area will be more useful.

UNITED STATES - MANUALS AND FLORAS.

These publications are designed to allow you to
identify the native plants of a certain designated
area. They may include keys only but most of them
have family, generic and specific descriptions of
varying completeness. When descriptions are given
the book is likely to be called a "manual", when
they are lacking it may be designated a "flora" but
this practice is not uniform. Unfortunately many of
these manuals and floras are out of print and a few
are as yet incomplete. When an area is very inadequately covered by a regional manual then more local
floras may be listed here.

A. Northeastern United States

1. Fernald, M. L. Gray's Manual of Botany.
    Eighth Edition, 1632 pages. American Book
    Co. 1950. Map I. 6 and IV. 3.

        Although designated as a revision this
    edition is essentially a new work. It is
    one volume and although rather bulky can
    still be easily carried around. For this
    and other reasons, "Gray's Manual" has been
    the favorite text for classes in its area
    for many years. Some of the species are ac-
    companied by small drawings, these usually
    of some diagnostic portion. Accepted vari-
    eties are listed and often a key is pre-
    sented to them. This increases the size of
    the publication and may not be of a special
    value to the beginning student. However,
    they add to the authoritativeness and com-
    pleteness and can be ignored if desired.
    The flora of adjacent Canada is included
    (See Canadian Floras).

2. Gleason, H. The New Britton and Brown Il-
    lustrated Flora of the Northeastern United
    States and Adjacent Canada. New York Botan-
    ical Garden. 1952. 3 volumes. Map I. 6
    and III. 3.

        The 3 volumes are rather bulky to carry
    in the field, and this fact combined with
    the necessary higher cost has resulted in
    the work being used more largely as a

reference than as a text. The keys and
descriptions are reasonably complete. Each
species is illustrated and the diagnostic
structure is usually indicated, often by en-
larging a portion of the plant. Although it
is stated in the preface that the work "has
been prepared primarily for the interested
laity rather than the professional botanist",
the publication remains a technical manual.

The new edition is a revision of the
Britton and Brown Illustrated Flora, Second
Edition, 1913. The older edition differed
from the new by including citations to orig-
inal sources and by including the states of
Kansas, Nebraska, South Dakota and North
Dakota to the west. The older work also ex-
tended much farther north into Canada (See
Canadian Floras).

B. Southeastern and Southcentral United States

1. Small, J. K. Manual of the Southeastern
    Flora. 1933. Published by the Author.
    New York. 1370 pages. Map I. 7.

        A conventional manual with keys and
    descriptions of seed plants (the ferns not
    included). The floral characters of each
    genus are illustrated. Although published
    after 1930 when the followers of the 2 codes
    finally reconciled their differences, un-
    fortunately the nomenclature still follows
    closest to the American Code Rules instead of
    the now generally used International Rules.

2. Small, J. K. Flora of the Southeastern
    United States. Second Edition 1913. Pub-
    lished by the Author. New York. 1,394
    pages. Map II. 4.

        This is the work on which the preceding
    revision was based. It is important still
    because it differs from the newer version as
    follows. (a) It includes the Pteriodophyta.
    (b) It extends west to the 100th meridian
    and accordingly includes Arkansas, Louisiana,
    most of Oklahoma and over one-half of Texas

104

(west of the eastern border of the Texas
Panhandle). The American Code of Nomenclature is followed.

3. Stemen, T. R. and Myers, W. S. Oklahoma
   Flora. Harlow Publishing Co. 1937. 706
   pages.

   Manual-like is the pattern with some of
the species illustrated. The descriptions
are short and the families Cyperaceae and
Gramineae are omitted. The American Code of
Nomenclature is followed.

4. Reeves, R. G. and Bain, D. C. Flora of
   Southcentral Texas. W. M. Wetch Manufacturing Company, Chicago, Ill. 1947. 298
   pages.

   A rather abbreviated manual covering an
irregular area in the Costal Plains of Texas
from Madison County extending southwest to
Bee and Guadaloupe Counties. The treatment
of the grasses is admittedly incomplete and
the Pteridophytes are omitted altogether.

   At this writing the flora of Texas is
very inadequately treated in any form. A
Flora of Texas is in preparation and several
parts have been issued to date. It is published by the Southern Methodist University,
University Press, Dallas, Texas.

C. Midwestern United States

1. Rydberg, P. A. Flora of the Prairies and
   Plains of Central North America. New York
   Bot. Garden. New York. 1932. 969 pages.
   Map II. 3.

   A conventional manual with keys and
descriptions. Many of the genera have one
species illustrated. The nomenclature follows the International Rules. A small portion of southcentral Canada is included.
(See Canadian Floras.)

2. Stevens, O. A. Handbook of North Dakota
Plants. Fargo, North Dakota. 1950. 324
pages.

Contains keys to families, genera and
species with rather brief descriptions of
each, except in genera with very few species.
Many plants are illustrated and some of the
characters used in the main family key are
accompanied by marginal drawings.

D. Western United States

1. Coulter, J. and Nelson, A. New Manual of
Botany of the Central Rocky Mountains (vascular plants). American Book Co. 1909.
646 pages. Map I. 4.

The keys and descriptions were kept
rather short which allowed this book to be a
size convenient for carrying around. The
nomenclature follows the International Rules.
A so-called conservative attitude is adopted
in the treatment of specific units.

2. Rydberg, P. A. Flora of the Rocky Mountains
and Adjacent Plains, Colorado, Utah, Wyoming,
Idaho, Montana, Saskatchewan, Alberta and
neighboring Parts of Nebraska, South Dakota,
North Dakota and British Columbia. Published
by the Author. New York. Second Edition
1922. 1143 pages. Map II. 2 and III. 2.

This second edition contains 33 pages of
additions and corrections but is otherwise
like the first. The American Code of Nomenclature is followed and the Author was what
some people call a "splitter", often dividing
the older "species" into several to many.
For that reason students may find this manual
difficult to use.

3. Tidestrom, I. and Kittell, Sister, T. A
Flora of Arizona and New Mexico. Catholic
University of America Press. Washington,
D. C. 1941. 897 pages.

106

This publication presents keys to the
families, genera and species. In addition
very abbreviated specific descriptions are
often given. The arrangement of the families
is unconventional with the Gymnosperms,
Dicotyledons and Monocotyledons presented in
that order, ending with the Pteridophytes.

4. Kearney, T. H. and Peebles, R. H. Arizona
   Flora. University of California Press.
   1951. 1032 pages.

   Contains keys to the families, genera
   and species of Arizona plants with descriptions to the families and genera only. The
   keys are exceptionally complete and accurate
   but are of the bracket instead of the indented type, and therefore harder for most
   botanists to use. The publication super-
   cedes the Author's "Flowering Plants and
   Ferns of Arizona" 1942.

5. Harrington, H. D. Manual of the Plants of
   Colorado. Sage Books, Denver, Colorado
   1954. 666 pages.

   Gives keys to families, genera and
   species. Each species is accompanied by a
   complete specific description as well as the
   geographical and altitudinal range within
   the State.

6. Tidestrom, I. Flora of Utah and Nevada.
   Contr. U. S. Herb. Vol. 25. 665 pages.
   1925.

   Provides the usual keys to families,
   genera and species but descriptions to the
   families only. The nomenclature follows the
   American Code.

7. Porter, C. L. Contributions Toward a Flora
   of Wyoming. Issued in numbered leaflets.
   University of Wyoming.

   These are mostly mimeographed (or with
   some similar process) each treating one
   family. The family description is usually
   accompanied by one or more diagrams or

drawings illustrating the floral type. The
genera are described but not the species.
The work is incomplete to date (1957).

8. Piper, Chas. V. Flora of the State of Washington. Contr. U. S. Nat. Herb. Vol. 11.
1906. 637 pages.

Keys to families, genera and species are
presented but no descriptions are given except to the newly described species. A list
of "specimens examined" is given for each
species. The nomenclature used is closest
to the rules adopted by the followers of the
American Code.

9. St. John, Harold. Flora of Southeastern
Washington and Adjacent Idaho. Student's
Book Corporation. Pullman, Washington 1937.
476 pages. Map I. 3.

Besides the usual keys this book has
descriptions to the families, genera and
species. The nomenclature follows the International Rules. An interesting feature
is the alphabetical arrangement of the genera
under the families, and the species under the
genera. This is designed to make each taxon
easier to locate.

10. Holmgren, A. H. Handbook of the Vascular
Plants of Northeastern Nevada. Utah State
Agri. College and U. S. Grazing Service.
1942. 214 pages. Mimeographed. Map I. 2.

Contains keys to the families, genera
and species with short descriptions to the
genera only. The nomenclature follows the
International Rules. The study includes all
of Elko County and the northern parts of
Eureka and Lander Counties.

11. Davis, Ray. Flora of Idaho. Wm. D. Brown
Company, Dubuque, Iowa. 1952. 828 pages.

This is manual-like with keys and descriptions to all the taxa. The specific
descriptions are reasonably complete. An

unusual feature of this work is that the
genera in each family and the species under
the genera are alphabetically arranged.

12. Peck, M. E. A Manual of the Higher Plants
of Oregon. Benfords and Mort. Portland,
Oregon. 1941. 866 pages.

   This book gives keys to and descriptions of the families, genera and species
of the state. The descriptions are reasonably complete and local description within
the state is given.

13. Abrams, L. and Ferris, R. An Illustrated Flora of
the Pacific States, Washington, Oregon and California. Stanford Univ. Press. 4 Vols. 1940-1960.
Map II. 2.

   The first volume was originally issued in 1923
but in 1940 was revised to conform with the International Rules of Nomenclature. Volume 4 contains the
family keys. The generic and specific keys, as well
as the family, generic and specific descriptions,
are very complete. Each species is accompanied by
an illustration, many original but often borrowed
from the Illustrated Flora of Britton and Brown.
The 4 volumes are rather bulky to carry in the field
but are invaluable as a source of reference.

14. Jepson, W. L. A Manual of the Flowering
Plants of California. Univ. of California,
Berkeley, Calif. 1923-1925. 1238 pages.

   A conventional manual with keys and
descriptions. Certain species are accompanied by illustrations, these well done. The
Pteridophytes are included in the work.

   A later book by the same author is the
"Flora of California" projected in 3 volumes. This is a more authoritative work
with bibliographic references but is not as
yet completed.

109

15. Munz, P. A. A Manual of Southern California Botany. J. W. Stacey, Inc. San Fran-
cisco. 1935. 642 pages. Map I. 1.

This is a regular manual with keys and
descriptions of the families, genera and
species of California south of a line from
Point Conception in Santa Barbara to north
of Death Valley on the east. Many of the
species are illustrated.

ALASKA AND CANADA - MANUALS AND FLORAS

1. Hulten, E. The Flora of the Aleutian Is-
lands and Westernmost Alaska Peninsula, with
Notes on the Flora of Commander Islands.
Stockholm. 1937. 397 pages.

A well annotated list of the species
included with detailed distributional in-
information. No keys or descriptions of the
477 species are provided.

2. Hulten, E. Flora of Alaska and Yukon.
Lunds univ. arssk. N. F. Avd. Lund. 1941-
1950. Parts I.-X. Map III. 1.

This is an annotated flora with keys
to species but with no keys to the larger
groups. No descriptions are included but
full synonomy and local distributional data
are presented including distributional maps
for each species. Notes concerning variations, differences from related species etc.
accompany many of the species.

3. Anderson, J. P. Flora of Alaska and Adjacent Parts of
Canada. Iowa State University Press. Ames. 1959.

An illustrated descriptive text of all vascular
plants known to occur within the region covered.
Presents keys to and descriptions of the families,
genera and species. Most species are illustrated
by original drawings. The parts of Canada covered
are the Yukon Territory and the extreme northwestern part of British Columbia.

4. Taylor, R. F. and E. L. Little, Jr. Pocket
   Guide to Alaska Trees. U. S. D. A. Forest
   Service, Agri. Handbook No. 55. June, 1950.
   63 pages.

   Semi-popular in nature but very useful.
   Contains descriptions and illustrations of
   30 species of trees with the distribution of
   each given. The key to the species is based
   mainly on vegetative characters. A winter
   key to the deciduous trees is presented and
   some selected references are listed at the
   end of the booklet. It is of pocket size
   and should be very useful to the student of
   Alaskan trees.

5. Macoun, J. Catalogue of Canadian Plants.
   Geol. and Nat. Hist. Survey of Canada. 3
   Volumes, 7 parts. Montreal, Canada. 1883-
   1902.

   An annotated list of the phanerogams
   and cryptogams of Canada including Alaska
   and Newfoundland. Parts I-V (Volumes 1-2),
   deals with 3209 species of vascular plants.
   No keys are included and descriptions are
   given to only a relatively few species but
   the information on local and general distribution is fairly complete. The work would
   hardly allow for student identification but
   would be of value as a check list of possibilities.

6. Forestry Branch. Native Trees of Canada.
   Bulletin 61. 4th Edition 1950. Dept. of
   Resources and Development, Canada.

   Gives descriptions to native species
   with photographs of habit, leaves, fruits
   etc. The local distribution is given on a
   map for each species. No keys are presented
   and the book is semi-popular in nature.

111

7. Louis-Marie, Pere. Flore-manuel de la province due quebec. 319 pages. Montreal, Canada. 1931. (Contrib. No. 23. Institut d'Oka).

   Elementary flora of the vascular plants of Quebec, in the form of keys. Text in French.

8. Marie-Victorin, Frere. Flore laurentienne. 917 pages. Montreal, Canada. 1935. Map III. 4.

   An annotated, illustrated descriptive flora of vascular plants, with keys. The text is in French. The area covered is in southern Quebec north to about Lake St. John.

9. Fernald, M. L. Gray's Manual of Botany. 8th Edition. 1632 pages. American Book Co., 1950. Map IV. 3.

   The 8th Edition includes southern Ontario and Quebec south of the 49th parallel of latitude and all of New Brunswick, Nova Scotia, Prince Edward Island and Newfoundland.

10. Gleason, H. The New Britton and Brown Illustrated Flora of the Northeastern United States and Adjacent Canada. New York Botanical Garden. 1952. 3 volumes. Map III. 3.

    This includes southern Ontario from a point east of Lake Superior and east along the 47th parallel latitude to the St. Lawrence River and all the area south of that river except Newfoundland.

11. Rydberg, P. A. Flora of the Prairies and Plains of Central North America. New York Botanical Garden. New York. 1932. 969 pages. Map IV. 2.

    This covers a small portion of southern Manitoba and southeastern Saskatchewan.

12. Rydberg, P. A. Flora of the Rocky Mountains and Adjacent Plains, Colorado, Utah, Wyoming, Idaho, Montana, Saskatchewan, Alberta and Neighboring Parts of Nebraska, South Dakota, North Dakota and British Columbia. Published by the Author. New York. Second Edition 1922. 1143 pages. Map III. 2.

This flora extends northward from the northwestern corner of Idaho to the 55th parallel latitude and then east to the eastern borders of Saskatchewan; then south to the United States. It includes the southern half of Saskatchewan and Alberta with a small strip of southeastern British Columbia.

13. Britton, N. L. and Brown, A. An Illustrated Flora of the Northern United States and Canada. Three Volumes. Chas. Scribner's Sons, New York. 1896. Second Edition 1913. Map V. 1.

This covers eastern Canada from Newfoundland and Labrador west to the eastern border of Saskatchewan. The revised edition of this work covers a more limited area in both Canada and the United States (See number 10).

Note: In the descriptive material opposite the 5 maps the letter and number in parenthesis (example - D-15) refers to the place in this chapter where a discussion of the particular manual or flora can be found.

113

Map I.

1. Munz, P. A. A Manual of Southern California Botany. (D-15)

2. Holmgren, A. H. Handbook of the Vascular Plants of Northeastern Nevada. (D-10)

3. St. John, H. Flora of Southeastern Washington and Adjacent Idaho. (D-9)

4. Coulter, J. and Nelson, A. New Manual of Botany of the Central Rocky Mountains. (D-1)

5. Coulter, J. Botany of Western Texas. (Contrib. U. S. Natl. Herb. vol. 2. 1891-1894).

6. A. Fernald, M. L. Gray's Manual of Botany.
      (A-1)

   B. Gleason, H. The New Britton and Brown Illustrated Flora of the Northeastern United States and Adjacent Canada. (A-2)

7. Small, J. K. Manual of the Southeastern Flora.
   (B-1)

Gleason, H. and Cronquist, A. Manual of Vascular Plants of Northeastern United States and Adjacent Canada. Van Norstrand Co. Princeton. 1963.

Seymour, F. C. The Flora of New England.
Charles Tuttle Co. Rutland, Vt. 1969.

Steyermark, J. A. Flora of Missouri.
Iowa State Univ. Press. Ames. 1963.

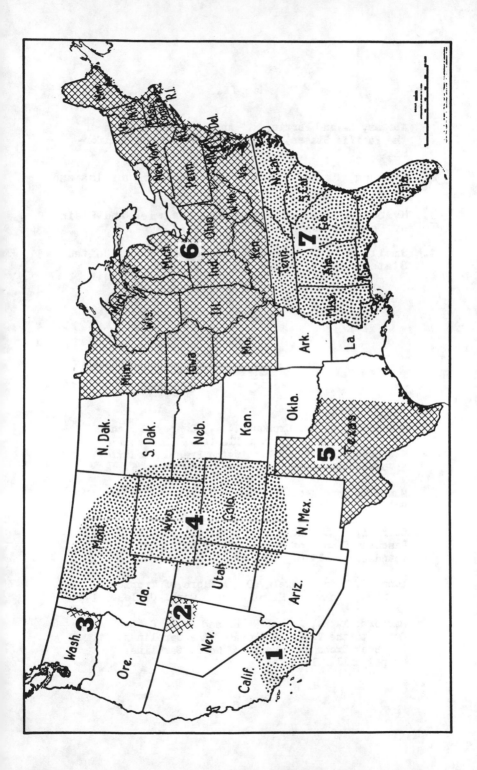

Map II.

1. Abrams, L. and Ferris, R. An Illustrated Flora of the Pacific States, Washington, Oregon and California. (D-13)

2. Rydberg, P. A. Flora of the Rocky Mountains and Adjacent Plains. (D-2)

3. Rydberg, P. A. Flora of the Prairies and Plains of Central North America. (C-1)

4. Small, J. K. Flora of the Southeastern United States. (B-2)

Hitchcock, C. L., Cronquist, A., Ownbey, M. and Thompson, J. W. Vascular Plants of the Pacific Northwest. Univ. of Washington Press. Seattle. 5 Vols. 1955-1969.

Munz, P. (and Keck, D. D.) A California Flora. Univ. of California Press. Berkeley. 1959.

Correll, D. S. and Johnston, M. C. Manual of the Vascular Plants of Texas. Texas Research Foundation. 1970.

Long, R. W. and Lakela, O. A Flora of Tropical Florida. Univ. of Miami Press. Coral Gables. 1971.

Radford, A. E., Ahles, H. E. and Bell, C. R. Guide to the Vascular Flora of the Carolinas. The Book Exchange. Univ. of North Carolina. Chapel Hill. 1964.

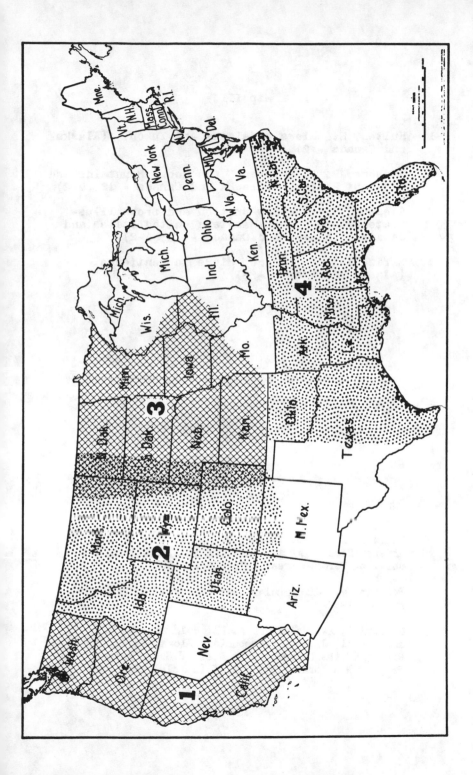

Map III.

1. Hulten, E. Flora of Alaska and Yukon. (Alaska and Canada - 2)

2. Rydberg, P. A. Flora of the Rocky Mountains and Adjacent Plains. (Alaska and Canada - 12; D-2)

3. Gleason, H. The New Britton and Brown Illustrated Flora of Northeastern United States and Canada. (Alaska and Canada - 10; A-2)

4. Marie-Victorin, Frere, Flore laurentienne. (Alaska and Canada - 8)

Wiggans, I. L. and Thomas, J. H. A Flora of the Alaskan Slope. Arctic Inst. of N. A. Sp. Pub. 4. Univ. of Toronto Press. Toronto. 1962.

Polunin, N. Circumpolar Arctic Flora. Oxford Univ. Press. 1959.

Cronquist, A., Holmgren, A. H., Holmgren, N. H. and Reveal, J. L. Intermountain Flora, Vascular Plants of the Intermountain West, U.S.A. Hafner Press. New York. 1972 Vol. I (6 Vols. projected)

Map IV.

1. Anderson, J. P. Flora of Alaska and Adjacent Parts of Canada. (Alaska and Canada - 3)

2. Rydberg, P. A. Flora of the Prairies and Plains of Central North America. (Alaska and Canada - 11; C-1)

3. Fernald, M. L. Gray's Manual of Botany. (Alaska and Canada - 9; A-1)

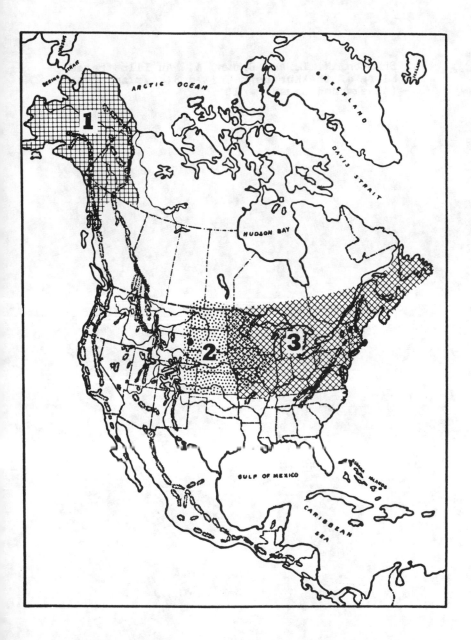

Map V.

1. Britton, N. L. and Brown, A. An Illustrated
   Flora of the Northern United States and Canada.
   (Alaska and Canada - 13)

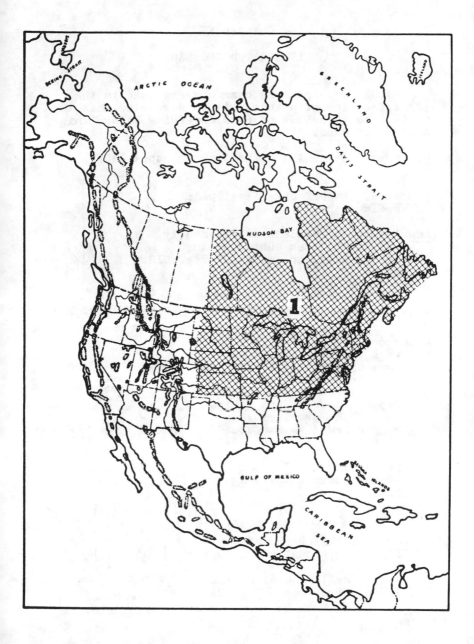

Chapter XV

ILLUSTRATED GLOSSARY

These are the more common terms used in the identification of plants. It is suggested that the preface to this book be read carefully before this chapter is used.

<u>A</u>. A prefix meaning without as in "apetalous".

<u>Abortive</u>. Imperfectly developed; rudimentary.

<u>Acaulescent</u>. Stemless or apparently so, or the stem subterranean; leaves basal or radical. Fig. 213.

ACAULESCENT
Fig. 213.

<u>Accessory Fruit</u>. A fleshy fruit with the fleshy part not a part of the pistil, like a strawberry where the receptacle is succulent and the ripened ovaries are achene-like. The drawings show such a fruit in surface view and split longitudinally with the achenes partly embedded in the fleshy receptacle, Fig. 214.

ACCESSORY FRUIT
Fig. 214.

<u>Accrescent</u>. Enlarging after flowering, usually the sepals.

<u>Acerose</u>. Needle-shaped as the leaves of spruce. Fig. 215.

SPRUCE   FIR
ACEROSE
Fig. 215.

Achene. A small, dry, 1-celled, 1-seeded indehiscent fruit, the seed attached to the pericarp at 1 place. Fig. 216.

PERICARP

SEED SHRUNKEN AWAY

ACHENE
Fig. 216.

Acicular. Shaped like a needle, as the "needle" of a pine tree. About the same as acerose.

Acorn. The 1-celled, 1-seeded fruit of oaks; consists of a cup-like base and the nut. Fig. 217.

ACORN OF OAK
Fig. 217.

Acrid. Sharp, irritating or biting to the taste.

Actinomorphic. Same as regular.

Acuminate. Tapering to the apex, the sides more or less pinched in before reaching the tip. Compare acute. Fig. 218.

ABRUPT   LONG

ACUMINATE
Fig. 218.

Acute. Tapering to the apex with the sides straight or nearly so; usually less tapering than acuminate. Fig. 219

NARROW   BROAD
ACUTE
Fig. 219.

Adherent. Same as adnate.

Adnate. The union of unlike parts, as an inferior ovary to the calyx tube. Compare connate.

Adventitious. Developing in an unusual or irregular

125

position, usually used for roots.

Aerial. In the air, as roots borne above the ground or water.

Aggregate. Crowded into a dense cluster but not united.

Aggregate Fruit. A fleshy fruit formed from several to many succulent pistils. The right-hand figure shows such a fruit in longitudinal section. Blackberry and raspberry are aggregate fruits. Fig. 220.

AGGREGATE FRUIT
Fig. 220.

Alpine. The area above timberline.

Alternate. Borne singly and not opposite - in leaves one at a node. Fig. 221.

Alveolar. Honeycombed. See alveolate.

Alveolate. Honeycombed. Fig. 222.

Ament. A spike or spike-like, usually pendulous inflorescence of unisexual flowers. Same as catkin. An ament would be either staminate or pistillate. Fig. 223.

ALTERNATE LEAVES
Fig. 221.

ALVEOLATE
Fig. 222.

AMENT
Fig. 223.

Amphibious. Usually growing submerged but may survive for long periods outside of the water.

Ampliate. Enlarged.

Anatropous. Upturned or inverted, said of an ovule with its micropyle next to the funiculus.

Androecium. The collective name for the stamens.

Anemophilous. Having wind-borne pollen.

Annual. Completing the life cycle in one growing season.

Annular. In the form of a ring. Fig. 224.

ANNULAR EMBRYO
Fig. 224.

Annulate. In the form of a ring. See annular.

Anterior. On the front side away from the axis.

Anther. The pollen-bearing part of the stamen. Fig. 225.

Fig. 225.

Anthesis. Period when the flower is open.

Antrorse. Directed forward or upward as of hairs. Fig. 226.

Apetalous. Lacking petals.

Apiculate. Ending in an abrupt slender tip which is not stiff. Fig. 227.

ANTRORSE HAIRS
Fig. 226.

Appendage. An attached secondary part to a main structure.

Appressed. Lying flat or close against something. Often used for hairs.

Approximate. Close together but not united.

APICULATE TIP
Fig. 227.

Aquatic. Living in water.

Arachnoid. Beset with cobwebby or en-
tangled hairs.

Arborescent. Approaching the size and
habit of a tree.

Arcuate. Arching or moderately curved
like a bow. Fig. 228.

ARCUATE LEGUME
Fig. 228.

Areola (pl. areolae). A small
space marked out upon or beneath the surface; often used
in leaves for the area between small veins. Also
spelled areole. Fig. 229.

AREOLA

RAISED AREA ON
CACTUS

AREOLAE
Fig. 229.

Areole. See areola.

Aril. An appendage growing at or about the
hilum of a seed. Compare caruncle.

Aristate. With an awn or stiff bristle,
usually at the apex. Fig. 230.

ARISTATE TIP
Fig. 230.

Aristulate. Minutely aristate.

Armed. Provided with thorns, spines,
prickles or sharp hairs.

Articulating. With a joint or node
separating at maturity by a clean
cut scar.

Ascending. Growing obliquely upward,
often curving upward usually at
about 40° - 60°. Fig. 231.

GROUND LINE
ASCENDING STEMS
Fig. 231.

Assurgent. Ascending.

Attenuate. Gradually narrowing to a tip or base, this usually narrow and slender. Fig. 232.

ATTENUATE
LEAF BASE
Fig. 232.

Auricle. An ear-shaped lobe or appendage. Fig. 233.

Auriculate. With auricles.

Awl-shaped. Tapering gradually upward from a broader base to a sharp point, narrowly triangular; usually used for small structures. Fig. 234.

Awn. A slender bristle-like organ usually at the apex of a structure. Fig. 235.

AURICLE AT BASE OF
LEAF BLADE
Fig. 233.

AWL-SHAPED LEAF
Fig. 234.

Fig. 235.

Axile. In the axil, the angle between an organ and its axis. See axillary.

Axile placentation. Ovules borne on the septum or septa of an ovary 2- or more- celled, usually near the center of the ovary. Fig. 236.

Axillary. In or related to the axis. Fig. 237.

AXILE PLACENTATION
Fig. 236.

AXILLARY FLOWER
Fig. 237.

Axis. The elongated central supporting structure, often specifically called a rachis.

Balsamiferous. Sticky and odoriferous, like balsam.

Banner. The upper, usually larger petal in a papilionaceous or "sweetpea type" flower. Fig. 238.

Barbed. With rigid short reflexed processes, like the barb of a fishhook. The drawing shows hairs barbed or barbellate. Fig. 239.

Barbellate. Finely barbed usually down the sides of the structure as well as at the apex.

Basifixed. Attached by the base. Compare versatile Fig. 240.

BANNER

WINGS

BANNER OF LEGUME FLOWER
Fig. 238.

BARBED BRISTLES
Fig. 239.

ANTHERS

BASIFIXED
Fig. 240.

VERSATILE

Bast bundle. See vascular bundle.

Beak. A hard of firm point or projection. Used for the ram-like projection on the keel of some legume flowers or the slender prolongation on the fruit of dandelion. (Taraxacum). Fig. 241.

BEAK ON KEEL OF LEGUME
Fig. 241. No. 1.

BEAK

BEAK ON FRUIT OF TARAXACUM
Fig. 241. No. 2.

Bearded. Furnished with long or stiff hairs.

Berry. A fleshy pulpy fruit with immersed seeds. Rather loosely used. The right-hand figure is a longitudinal section. Fig. 242.

BERRY
Fig. 242.

Bicolored. Of 2 rather sharply contrasting colors.

Biennial. Living for 2 years.

Bifid. Two-cleft or 2-lobed, usually at the apex. Fig. 243.

BIFID APEX
OF PETAL
Fig. 243.

Bifurcate. Divided into 2 forks or branches. Fig. 244.

Bilabiate. Two-lipped. Fig. 245.

Bipinnate. Doubly or twice-pinnate, the primary divisions once-again pinnate. Fig. 246.

BIFURCATE
STYLE
Fig. 244.

BILABIATE COROLLA
Fig. 245.

BIPINNATE LEAF
Fig. 246.

Bisexual. Having both stamens and pistils, usually used for a flower. Same as perfect.

Biturbinate. Rather top-shaped but the widest part not directly at one end. Fig. 247.

BITURBINATE FRUIT
Fig. 247.

Bladder. An inflated, thin-walled structure.

Blade. The expanded usually flat portion of a leaf or petal. Compare sheath, petiole and claw. Both a leaf and a petal are figured. Fig. 248.

BLADE
PETIOLE
STIPULES
BLADE
BLADE
CLAW
Fig. 248.

131

Bloom. A whitish powdery, glaucous, usually waxy covering of a surface. Also used in reference to a flower.

Bract. A more or less modified leaf situated near a flower or inflorescence. Fig. 249.

FLOWER
BRACT
BRACTS
Fig. 249.

Bracteate. Having bracts.

Bracteolate. With bractlets.

Bracteole. Same as bractlet.

Bractlet. A secondary bract as one on the pedicel of a flower, usually smaller than the bracts. Also sometimes used for a very small bract. Fig. 250.

BRACTLET
BRACT
BRACTLET
Fig. 250.

Bristle. A stiff hair-like structure on the order of a pig bristle. Fig. 251.

BRISTLES
Fig. 251.

Bud. The rudimentary state of a stem or branch. Also used for an unexpanded flower. Fig. 252.

SCALES
SEPALS
TREE BUD   FLOWER BUD
Fig. 252.

Bulb. A subterranean leaf-bud with fleshy scales like an onion. The drawing is of a bulb in longitudinal section. Fig. 253.

BULB
Fig. 253.

132

Bulblet. A small bulb especially one borne above the ground as an onion-set.

Bur. A seed or fruit bearing spines or prickles, these usually hooked or barbed. Fig. 254.

BUR
Fig. 254.

Bush. A low thick shrub without a distinct trunk.

Caducous. Falling off unusually early as compared with similar structures in general.

Caespitose. Growing in tufts. Also written cespitose. The illustration shows the base of a plant with many caespitose stems. Fig. 255.

CAESPITOSE
Fig. 255.

Callous. Having a hard texture, often swollen.

Callus. A hard protuberance or callosity. In grasses the indurated downward extension of the lemma, morphologically a part of the rachilla. Fig. 256.

CALLUS TIPPED
LEAF TEETH
Fig. 256.

Calyculate. Having bracts around the calyx or involucre, these usually smaller.

Calyx. The outer series of the perianth, used especially when it differs in size, shape or color from the inner (or petals). Fig. 257.

Calyx tube. That part of the calyx where the sepals are united. Also used for the hypanthium.

Campanulate. Bell-shaped, rather cup-shaped with a flaring rim. Fig. 258.

CALYX-OF
SEPALS
Fig. 257.

CAMPANULATE
COROLLA
Fig. 258.

133

Canaliculate. Longitudinally chan-
neled or grooved. The drawing
shows a fruit cut transversely.
Fig. 259.

CANALICULATE
Fig. 259.

Canescent. With gray or white short
hairs, short-hoary. Often loosely used to mean any gray or white
surface. Fig. 260.

CANESCENT
Fig. 260.

Capillary. Very slender and hair-like.

Capitate. In a globular or head-shaped
cluster. Fig. 261.

CAPITATE
FLOWERS
Fig. 261.

Capitellate. Head-like; a diminutive of capitate.

Capsule. A dry dehiscent fruit made up of more than
1 carpel. Fig. 262.

LOCULICIDAL   PORICIDAL   SEPTICIDAL
CIRCUMSCISSLE
CAPSULES
Fig. 262.

Carinate. Keeled with one or more
longitudinal ridges. Fig. 263.

CARINATE FRUIT
Fig. 263.

134

Carpel. A simple pistil formed from 1 sporophyll, or that part of a compound pistil formed from 1 sporophyll. See figures 47 and 48.

Carpophore. The slender prolongation of the floral axis which in Umbelliferae supports the pendulous carpels. Fig. 264.

CARPOPHORE
Fig. 264.

Cartilaginous. Firm and tough but elastic like cartilage.

Caruncle. An excrescence or appendage at or about the hilum of a seed. Usually fleshy and less tendril-like than an aril. Fig. 265.

CARUNCLE
Fig. 265.

Caryopsis. A dry, 1-seeded, indehiscent fruit in which the seed is grown fast to the pericarp at all points.

Castaneous. Of a chestnut or dark brown color.

Catkin. An ament. Fig. 266.

Caudate. With a slender tail-like appendage. Fig. 267.

Caudex (pl. **caudices**). The persistent, often woody base of an otherwise annual herbaceous stem.

Caulescent. Having a manifest leafy stem above ground. Compare with **acaulescent**. Fig. 268.

AMENT-
CATKIN
Fig. 266.

CAUDATE
LEAF TIP
Fig. 267.

CAULINE
LEAF

RADICAL
LEAF

CAULESCENT PLANT
Fig. 268.

135

Cauline. Of or pertaining to the stem.

Cauloid. Stem-like.

Cell. A microscopic structural unit of a plant. When used in connection with a pistil then the same as **locule.**

Cellular. Made up of small pits or compartments.

Centimeter (abbreviation **cm.**). Ten millimeters or about 2.54 of an inch.

Chaff. A thin dry scale or bract. One of the bracts between the individual flowers in the head of the **Compositae.**

Chaffy. Possessing or resembling chaff.

Chartaceous. Having the texture of stiff writing paper or parchment.

Chlorophyll. The green pigment associated with photosynthesis.

Ciliate. Beset with a marginal fringe of hairs (cilia). Fig. 269.

CILIATE LEAF

Fig. 269.

Ciliolate. Ciliate but the hairs minute.

Circinate. Coiled from the tip downward, resembling the upper end of a violin. The figure shows an unfolding fern leaf (or frond). Fig. 270.

Circumscissile. Dehiscing in a transverse circular line, the top separating like the lid of a pill box. Fig. 271.

CIRCINATE FERN FROND

Fig. 270.

CIRCUMSCISSILE CAPSULE

Fig. 271.

136

Clasping. Describing a sessile leaf with the lower edges of the blade partly surrounding the stem. Fig. 272.

Clavate. Club-shaped and widest nearer the apex. Fig. 273.

Claw. The narrowed base or stalk to some petals. The expanded portion would be the blade. Fig. 274.

CLASPING LEAF

Fig. 272.

CLAVATE

Fig. 273.

CLAW OF PETAL

Fig. 274.

Cleft. Cut in about $\frac{1}{2}$ way to the midvein or base (as on a leaf), especially when the sinus is sharp. The left leaf is pinnately cleft, the right leaf palmately cleft. Fig. 275.

CLEFT LEAVES
Fig. 275.

Gleistogamous. Fertilized in the bud, the flower never opening.

Coalescent. Union of parts of the same kind.

Cochleate. Coiled or shaped like a snail shell.

Coerulean. Blue or bluish.

Collateral. Situated at the side of something.

Column. A group of united filaments as in Malvaceae. Also the coalesced style and filaments in the Orchidaceae.

Coma. A tuft of hairs especially at the
tips of seeds. Fig. 276.

COMA
Fig. 276.

Commissure. The surface by
which 1 carpel joins another
in Umbelliferae. The drawing shows a fruit cut transversely. Fig. 277.

COMMISSURE
Fig. 277.

Comose. Furnished with a
tuft of hairs or coma.

Complete. A flower with
sepals, petals, stamens
and pistils present.

Compound leaf. A leaf completely separated into
2 or more leaflets.
Fig. 278.

COMPOUND LEAVES
Fig. 278.

Compound ovary. An ovary with
2 or more carpels.

Compressed. Flattened especially laterally.

Conduplicate. Folded lengthwise down the middle. The
leaf in the drawing has been
cut transversely.

CONDUPLICATE
LEAF
Fig. 279.

Cone. The dry multiple fruit of pine, spruce etc., consisting of overlapping scales. Same as strobilus. Also used as a shape "cone-shaped". Fig. 280.

CONE
Fig. 280.

Confluent. Running together; blending in one.

Conical. Cone-shaped, attached at the broad end.

Connate. The union of like structures. Compare adnate.

Connective. That portion of a stamen that connects the 2 halves of an anther. Fig. 281.

ANTHER
CONNECTIVE
Fig. 281.

Connivent. Converging; in close contact but not actually united by tissue.

Continuous. Said of a rachis or axis that does not break up at joints at maturity. Compare articulate.

Contorted. Twisted or bent or twisted on itself.

Contracted. Said of an inflorescence that is narrow and dense with short or appressed branches.

Convolute. Rolled up longitudinally; technically one edge inside the other but loosely used especially in grasses. The drawing shows a leaf cut transversely. Fig. 282.

CONVOLUTE
LEAF
Fig. 282.

Cordate. Of a conventional heart shape;
the point apical. Compare obcordate.
Fig. 283.

CORDATE LEAF
Fig. 283.

Coriaceous. Texture of leather.

Corm. A thickened, vertical solid
underground stem. Compare bulb.
The drawing shows a surface view.
Fig. 284.

SOLID

ROOTS

CORM
Fig. 284.

Corolla. The inner series of the floral
envelope; collective name for petals.

Corona. An appendage or extrusion standing between the corolla and the
stamens. Also called a "crown".

Corrugated. Wrinkled or in folds.
Fig. 285.

CORRUGATED
Fig. 285.

Cortical. Pertaining to the outer covering.

Corymb. A flat-topped or convex open inflorescence;
technically a contracted raceme. Fig. 286.

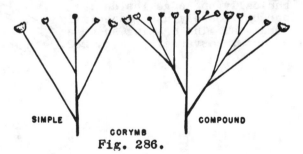

SIMPLE

COMPOUND

CORYMB
Fig. 286.

140

Corymbiform. Shaped like a corymb.

Corymbose. Borne in corymbs or corymb-like.

Cotyledon. The embryo leaf in a seed, often functioning as the first leaf of a seedling.

Cremocarp. The dry fruit of the Umbelliferae (carrot) family, made up of 2 one-seeded mericarps which separate at maturity. Also called a **schizocarp.** Fig. 287.

STYLOPODIUM

MERICARP

CARPOPHORE

CREMOCARP

Fig. 287.

Crenate. Toothed with teeth rounded at apex. Fig. 288.

Crenulate. Crenate with small teeth.

Crest. An elevated ridge or projection on the surface.

Crown. An inner appendage to a petal or throat of a corolla. Also used for the persistent base of a tufted perennial plant especially a grass. Fig. 289.

Crustose. Of a hard and brittle texture.

Cucullate. Hooded or hood-shaped; like a cowl. Fig. 290.

CRENATE

Fig. 288.

CROWN

CROWN OF PETAL

Fig. 289.

CUCULLATE PETAL

Fig. 290.

Culm. The specialized stem of grasses, sedges and rushes.

Cuneate. Wedge-shaped; rather narrowly triangular, the acute angle downward. Fig. 291.

Fig. 291.

Cuspidate. Tipped with an abrupt, short, sharp, firm point. Compare mucronate. Fig. 292.

CUSPIDATE
LEAF TIP
Fig. 292.

Cyathium. The ultimate inflorescence in the genus Euphorbia consisting of unisexual flowers congested within a cup-shaped involucre. Fig. 293.

CYATHIUM OF
EUPHORBIA
Fig. 293.

Cyme. A flower cluster, often convex or flat-topped, in which the central or terminal flower blooms earliest. Fig. 294.

CYMES
Fig. 294.

Cymose. Bearing cymes or cyme-like.

Cymule. A small cyme or portion of one.

Deciduous. Falling away, not persistent or evergreen.

Decompound. More than once-compound, the primary divisions again completely separated.

142

Decumbent. Reclining on the ground
but with the end ascending;
used for stems. Fig. 295.

DECUMBENT STEM

Fig. 295.

Decurrent. Extending downward from
the point of insertion; said of
a leaf decurrent on the stem.
Fig. 296.

ATTACHED
AREA

DECURRENT LEAF
Fig. 296.

Deflexed. Bent or turned abruptly downward or backward. Same as reflexed.

Dehiscent. Opening by definite pores or
slits to discharge the contents.

Deliquescent. A type of branching with
no well defined central axis running
from base to apex.

Deltoid. Shaped like the Greek letter
Delta △ , attached at the center of
one side. Fig. 297.

DELTOID LEAF
Fig. 297.

Dense. Said of inflorescences
where the flowers are crowded.

Dentate. Toothed with the teeth
directed outward. Sometimes
loosely used for any large
teeth. Fig. 298.

DENTATE
Fig. 298.

Denticles. With minute, usually
fragile teeth.

Denticulate. Dentate with small
teeth. Fig. 299.

DENTICULATE
MARGIN
Fig. 299.

143

Depauperate. Starved or stunted; said of small
plants growing under unfavorable conditions.

Depressed. More or less flattened
from above.

Diadelphous. Stamens in 2 often unequal sets. Fig. 300.

DIADELPHOUS STAMENS
Fig. 300.

Dichotomous. Two-forked, the branches equal or
nearly so. Fig. 301.

Didymous. Twin-like; in equal pairs.

Didynamous. Stamens in 2 pairs of unequal length.
The drawing shows a two-lipped corolla with 4
stamens protruding beyond the lower lip.
Fig. 302.

Diffuse. Loosely or widely spreading.

Digitate. Compound with the parts radiating out
from a common point like the fingers on a hand.
Same as palmate. Fig. 303.

DICHOTOMOUS
BRANCHING
Fig. 301.

DIDYNAMOUS STAMENS
Fig. 302.

DIGITATE
LEAFLETS

Fig. 303.

Dimorphic. In 2 forms.

Dimorphous. With 2 forms.

Dioecious. Flowers unisexual, the staminate and
pistillate borne on separate plants.

Disarticulating. The parts separating at maturity.
Compare articulating.

Disc. Same as disk.

Discoid. Resembling a disk. A discoid head in
Compositae is one where no ray flowers are present.

Disk. An enlargement or prolongation of the receptacle of a
flower around the pistil, sometimes made up of coalesced
nectaries of staminodia. In the
Compositae the central part of
the head bearing regular tubular flowers. Fig. 304.

DISK
Fig. 304.

Disk flowers. The regular
tubular flowers on the
heads of Compositae.
Compare ray-flowers or
ligules. Fig. 305.

DISK FLOWERS IN
COMPOSITAE
Fig. 305.

Dissected. Cut or divided into numerous and usually narrow segments.
Too varied to draw.

Distal. The end opposite the point of
attachment.

Distichous. In 2 vertical ranks, usually conspicuously so. Fig. 306.

DISTICHOUS
LEAVES
Fig. 306.

Distinct. Separate like parts,
these not at all united
to each other. Compare
connate.

Diurnal. Occurring in the
daytime.

Divaricate. Widely spreading or diverging.

Divided. Deeply lobed, the
sinuses extending to the
base of the leaf or to
the midrib; nearly com-
pound. Fig. 307.

PINNATE   PALMATE
DIVIDED LEAF MARGINS
Fig. 307.

Dolabriform. Pick-shaped; said of hairs apparently attached at their middle. Fig. 308.

DOLABRIFORM HAIRS

Fig. 308.

Dorsal. Pertaining to the back or outer surface of an organ.

Dorsiventral. On a plane running from the dorsal to the ventral side of a structure. Opposite to lateral.

ECTOCARP
MESOCARP
ENDOCARP
SEED

Drupe. A fleshy indehiscent, 1-seeded fruit, the inner layer of the pericarp stony. The drawing shows a drupe in longitudinal section. Fig. 309.

DRUPE

Fig. 309.

Druplet. A diminutive drupe, as the small parts of a raspberry fruit.

E. A prefix meaning lacking or without.

Eccentric. Not situated at the central axis; off-center.

Echinate. Provided with prickles. Fig. 310.

ECHINATE

Fig. 310.

Echinulate. With minute prickles.

Ellipsoid. A solid body, elliptic in outline.

Elliptic. Shaped like an ellipse; widest in center and the 2 ends equal. Loosely used. The drawing shows an average example but the leaf can be longer and narrower and still be elliptic. Fig. 311.

ELLIPTIC LEAF

Fig. 311.

Elliptical. Same as elliptic.

146

Emarginate. With a shallow notch at the apex. Fig. 312.

Embryo. The rudimentary plant within a seed.

Endemic. Confined to a limited geographical area.

Endocarp. The inner layer of the pericarp when this is observable. For an example see drawing of a drupe.

Endosperm. Substance surrounding the embryo in a seed.

Ensiform. Shaped like a sword, as the leaf of Iris. Fig. 313.

Entire. Margins without teeth or lobes. Fig. 314.

EMARGINATE
APEX
Fig. 312.

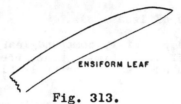

ENSIFORM LEAF
Fig. 313.

ENTIRE MARGIN
Fig. 314.

Entomophilous. Pollinated by insects.

Ephemeral. Lasting for one day or less.

Epidermis. The outer layer of cells.

Epigynous. Growing on the summit of the ovary or appearing to do so. The drawing shows a flower in longitudinal section. Fig. 315.

INFERIOR
OVARY

EPIGYNOUS
FLOWER
Fig. 315.

Equitant. Leaves that are conduplicate and in 2 ranks; also 2-ranked leaves, flattened with edges toward and away from the axis. Fig. 316.

Erose. Margin irregular as if gnawed. Fig. 317.

EQUITANT LEAVES
Fig. 316.

EROSE
Fig. 317.

Erosulate. More of less erose.

Even-pinnate. A pinnately compound leaf ending in a pair of leaflets, hence presumably with an even number of leaflets. Fig. 318.

Evergreen. Bearing green leaves throughout the year. Compare deciduous.

Ex. A prefix meaning lacking or without.

EVEN PINNATE LEAF
Fig. 318.

Excurrent. Running out or beyond, as a nerve of a leaf projecting out beyond the margin. Also used for habit of a tree where there is one main unbranched axis from bottom to top as in a spruce or fir tree. Fig. 319. and Fig. 320.

Excurved. Curving outward or away from the axis.

Exfoliating. Peeling off in thin layers.

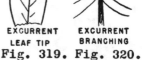

EXCURRENT LEAF TIP
Fig. 319.

EXCURRENT BRANCHING
Fig. 320.

Exocarp. The outer layer of the pericarp. For an example see the drawing of a drupe.

Exotic. Not native, introduced from another area. Compare indigenous.

Explanate. Spread out flat.

Exserted. Projecting beyond a surrounding organ, as a stamen exserted from a corolla. Compare included. Fig. 321.

EXSERTED
STAMENS

Fig. 321.

Extrorse. Facing outward, often used for anthers turned away from the center of the flower.

Falcate. Scythe- or scimiter-shaped, curved sidewise and flat, tapering upwards; asymmetric. Fig. 322.

FALCATE LEAF

Fig. 322.

Fan-shaped. Shaped like an opened folding fan; triangular with the upper side convex. Fig. 323.

Farinaceous. Starchy; mealy.

Farinose. Covering with a mealy usually whitish substance.

FAN SHAPED LEAF

Fig. 323.

PINE
FASCICLED
LEAVES

Fig. 324.

Fascicled. Borne in close bundles or clusters. Fig. 324.

Fastigiate. Erect or near together with a broom-like effect.

Fern-like. Used of a leaf dissected or divided into narrow segments like many ferns.

Fertile. Capable of producing fruit and seeds; a
fertile flower may be pistillate or perfect.

Fetid. With a disagreeable odor.

Fibrillose. With fine fibers. Sometimes written
fibrillate.

Fibrous. Composed of, or resembling
fibers.

Filament. Any thread-like body; used especially for that part of the stamen
that supports the anther. Fig. 325.

FILAMENT
OF STAMEN
Fig. 325.

Filamentose. Composed of threads. Also
written filamentous.

Filiferous. Producing or bearing thread-
like growths.

Filiform. Thread-like; long, slender
and terete.

Fimbriate. Margins with a fringe of
hairs, these longer and coarser
than ciliate. Fig. 326.

FIMBRIATE MARGIN
Fig. 326.

Fimbrilla (pl. fimbrillae). A single unit
of a marginal fringe.

Fistulose. Hollow and cylindrical like
onion leaves, often rather enlarged.
Also written fistulous. Fig. 327.

FISTULOSE
STEM
Fig. 327

Flabellate. Same as fan-shaped.

Flabelliform. Same as fan-shaped.

Flaccid. Lax and weak; without rigidity.

150

Flange. A projecting edge or rim; edge
     flaring and conspicuous. Fig. 328.

Fig. 328.

Flexuose. Same as flexuous.

Flexuous. Bent alternately in opposite directions,
     usually not strongly so. Fig. 329.

Floccose. Clothed with loose tufts of wool-like
     hair, this not uniform over the entire surface.
     Fig. 330.

Floral envelope. The collective name for the sepals
     and petals. Same as perianth.

Floret. A small flower especially one in a dense
     cluster. Also a special term for a grass flower
     with its lemma and palea included.

Floricane. The flowering and fruiting cane (stem)
     of a bramble (genus Rubus).

Floriferous. Bearing flowers.

Fluted. With grooves or furrows. Fig. 331.

FLOCCOSE

Fig. 330.

FLEXUOUS STEM
Fig. 329.

FLUTED STEM
Fig. 331.

Foliaceous. Leaf-like especially in color.

151

-foliate. Having leaves.

-foliolate. Having leaflets.

Follicle. A dry fruit with 1 carpel and splitting
    down one side only. Fig. 332.

Fornix (pl. fornices). Small arching crests in the
    throat of a corolla. The illustration shows the
    corolla tube split and flattened out. Fig. 333.

Fovea. (pl. foveae). Small depressions or pits.
    Fig. 334.

FORNIX

STAMEN

COROLLA
TUBE

FOVEA

FOLLICLE

Fig. 332.

FORNICES

Fig. 333.

Fig. 334.

Free. Not adnate; unlike parts not connected.

Free central placenta. The ovary is one-celled and
    the ovules are borne on a central stalk not con-
    nected at the top. Both a longitudinal and
    cross-section are figured. Fig. 335.

Frond. Leaf of a fern. In Lemnaceae the expanded
    thallus-like stem which functions as a leaf.
    Fern leaves are usually more dissected or de-
    compound than in the one illustrated. (See
    Fig. 102 also). Fig. 336.

Fruit. The ripened ovary and
    any other structures that
    enclose it at maturity.

Fruticose. Shrub-like; at
    least somewhat woody.
    Also written frutescent.

Fugacious. Falling or fad-
    ing very early. About
    the same as caducous.

OVARY

PLACENTA

OVULE

FREE CENTRAL
PLACENTAE
Fig. 335.

FERN FROND
Fig. 336.

Fulvous. Dull yellow; yellow tinged with brown or gray.

Funiculus (pl. funiculi). The ovule stem or attachment structure. The ovary is shown in longitudinal section. Fig. 337.

Fig. 337.

Funnelform. With the tube widening upward passing gradually into the limb. Fig. 338.

Fig. 338.

Furfuraceous. Resembling flakes or grains of bran; scurfy.

Fuscous. Grayish-brown or dusky-brown.

Fusiform. Spindle-shaped; broadest at the middle and tapering both ways. Fig. 339.

FUSIFORM

Fig. 339.

Galea. A hooded or helmet-shaped part of the perianth, usually the upper lip of an irregular corolla. Fig. 340.

Galeate. Shaped like a galea or helmet.

Gametophyte. The sexual stage in plants which bear sperm and eggs. Used particularly for the prothallus of ferns.

Fig. 340.

Gamopetalous. Petals more or less united. Same as sympetalous.

Gamophyllous. The leaves or leaf-like organs more
     or less united one to another.

Gamosepalous. The sepals more or less united.

Geminate. Equal, in pairs like twins.

Gemma (pl. gemmae). A bud
     or bud-like body by
     which some plants pro-
     pagate themselves.

Geniculate. Bent abruptly
     like knee or stove pipe
     bend. Fig. 341.

GENICULATE
BEND OF STEM

SAC ON
ONE
SIDE

GIBBOUS CALYX

Gibbous. Enlarged, humped
     or swollen on one side. Fig. 341.
     Fig. 342.

Fig. 342.

Glabrate. Becoming glabrous in age.

Glabrescent. About the same as glabrate.

Glabrous. No hairs present at all; also used for
     smooth.

Gland. A secreting surface or structure, or an ap-
     pendage having the general appearance of such an
     organ.

Glandular. Bearing glands. A gland-
     ular hair has an enlargement like
     a hat pin at the apex. Fig. 343.

GLANDULAR HAIRS

Fig. 343.

Glaucescent. Tending to be glaucous; somewhat
     glaucous.

Glaucous. Covered with a whitish or bluish waxy
     covering; this should readily rub off but the
     term is sometimes loosely used for any whitish
     surface.

154

Globose. Shaped like a globe, like a model of the earth. The drawing shows the two halves. Fig. 344.

Glochid. A barbed hair or bristle; usually used for the minute bristles in Opuntia. Fig. 345.

GLOBOSE GLOCHIDS
Fig. 344. Fig. 345

Glochidiate. Barbed at the tip.

Glomerate. Crowded, congested or compactly clustered.

Glomerule. A dense crowded cluster, usually of flowers.

Glume. A chaff-like bract; used particularly for the 2 lower empty bracts of a grass spikelet.

Glutinous. Covered with a sticky glue-like or gummy exudation.

Grain. A swollen, seed-like structure as on the fruit of some species of Rumex; also used as a synonym for caryopsis. Fig. 346.

VALVE-
ENLARGED
SEPAL

GRAIN

RUMEX FRUIT
Fig. 346.

Granulate. Composed of, or appearing to be covered by small granules. Same as granulose.

Granule. A minute rounded object.

Granuliferous. Composed of, or covered with very minute granules.

Grass-like. Resembling grasses; usually used for sedges and rushes.

Grenadin. A conspicuous orange- or brick-red color most characteristic of the petals of Sphaeralcea.

Gynobase. An enlargement or prolongation of the receptacle bearing the ovary. The flower in the drawing has been cut in half longitudinally with only two of the four nutlets showing. Fig. 347.

GYNOBASE IN
BORAGINACEAE
Fig. 347.

Gynoecium. A collective name for the pistils.

Halberd-shaped. Same as hastate.

Hastate. Arrow-head shaped but with the basal lobes pointing outward instead of backward. Used either for a shape or to describe the base alone. Fig. 348.

HASTATE LEAF
Fig. 348.

Haustoria. Root-like sucking attachments of parasitic plants like Cuscuta (dodder).

Head. A dense cluster of sessile or nearly sessile flowers or fruits on a very short axis; used especially for the involucrate inflorescence in Compositae.

Herb. A plant with no persistent woody stem above ground; also a plant used in seasoning and medicine.

Herbaceous. Having the characteristic of a herb; also leaf-like in color or texture.

Hermaphroditic. A flower with both stamens and pistils. Same as perfect and bisexual.

Heteromorphous. Of more than 1 kind or form.

Heterostyled. With more than 1 length of style.

Hilum. The scar or point of attachment of a seed. Fig. 349.

HILUM
Fig. 349.

156

Hirsute. With moderately coarse and stiff hairs. Fig. 350.

Hirsutulose. Same as hirsutulous.

Hirsutulous. Somewhat hirsute.

Hirtellous. Minutely hirsute.

Hispid. With stiff and rigid bristles or bristle-like hairs, these usually stiff enough to penetrate the skin. Fig. 351.

Hispidulous. Minutely hispid.

HIRSUTE

Fig. 350.

HISPID

Fig. 351.

HOOKED APEX OF FRUIT

Fig. 352.

HORNED FRUIT

Fig. 353.

Hoary. Covered with white or gray short fine hairs.

Homomorphous. Of only 1 form or kind.

Hooked. Abruptly curved at tip. Fig. 352.

Horn. A stiff tapering appendage somewhat like the horn of a cow. Fig. 353.

Hyaline. Thin, dry and transparent or translucent.

Hydrophyte. A plant that grows in water. Compare mesophyte and xerophyte.

Hygroscopic. Altering form or position due to changes in moisture content.

Hypanthium. An enlargement or elongation of the floral axis below the calyx, commonly partly or completely enclosing the pistils; when this occurs the ovary is here considered to be inferior. Fig. 354.

OVARY SUPERIOR   OVARY INFERIOR

HYPANTHIUM

Fig. 354.

Hypogynous. Situated on the receptacle below the ovary; a flower having the petals and stamens so situated. Fig. 355.

HYPOGYNOUS
Fig. 355.

Imbricate. Partly overlapping like shingles on a roof, either vertically or laterally. The drawing to the right shows a cross-section of lateral imbrication. Fig. 356.

IMBRICATE
Fig. 356.

Immersed. Growing submerged in water.

Imperfect flowers. Lacking either stamens or pistils. Compare perfect, unisexual and bisexual.

Incised. Cut sharply and usually irregularly with sharp sinuses, deeper than teeth but seldom as deep as ½ way in to the base or midrib. The leaf at the left is pinnately incised, the one at the right is palmately so. Fig. 357.

INCISED LEAF MARGINS

Fig. 357.

Included. Not at all protruding from the surrounding organ. The right figure shows a corolla split down one side and rolled flat. Fig. 358.

INCLUDED STAMENS
Fig. 358.

Incurved. Curved toward the axis or attachment.

Indehiscent. Remaining persistently closed; not opening by definite lines or pores.

Indigenous. Native to the area. Compare exotic.

Indurated. Hardened and stiffened.

Indusium (pl. indusia). The thin scale-like out-
     growth of the fern leaf forming a covering for
     the young sorus. Sometimes the inrolled margin
     functions as an indusium.

Inferior ovary. One that is adnate to
     the hypanthium or calyx tube, ap-
     pearing to be sunken in the stem, the
     flower parts appearing to come off
     from above the ovary; used here in
     the broad sense. Fig. 359.

INFERIOR OVARY
Fig. 359.

Inflated. Bladder-like; enlarged with
     thin walls. Fig. 360.

SEED

INFLATED POD
Fig. 360.

Inflexed. Turned abruptly or bent inwards; incurved.

Inflorescence. The flowering part of a plant, almost
     always used for a flower cluster.

Infrastipular. Situated below the stipules; used in
     Rosa when a pair of prickles below the node is
     enlarged or conspicuous because of the absence
     or scarcity of other prickles. Fig. 361.

Innovation. A basal offshoot from the main stem,
     shorter and less modified than a rhizome or
     stolon; in grasses an incomplete young shoot.
     Fig. 362.

INFRASTIPULAR
PRICKLES
Fig. 361.

PRIMARY
PLANT

INNOVATION
Fig. 362.

Internode. The portion of a stem or other structure between 2 nodes. Fig. 363.

Interrupted. Not continuous. Usually used for pinnately compound leaves where small leaflets are interspersed among the larger ones. Fig. 364.

Introduced. A plant brought in intentionally from another area, as for purposes of cultivation. Such a plant may later escape and persist.

Introrse. Turned in or facing inward, as an anther turned in toward the center of a flower. Fig. 365.

INTERNODE OF STEM
Fig. 363.

INTERRUPTEDLY PINNATE LEAF
Fig. 364.

INTRORSE ANTHERS
Fig. 365.

Involucel. A secondary involucre as in Umbelliferae. Fig. 366.

Involucrate. With an involucre.

Involucre. A whorl of distinct or united leaves or bracts subtending a flower or an inflorescence. Fig. 367.

Involute. Both edges inrolled toward the midnerve on the upper surface; loosely used in grasses for any leaf rolled on the upper surface. Compare revolute. Fig. 368.

INVOLUCEL
Fig. 366.

INVOLUCRE
Fig. 367.

INVOLUTE LEAF
Fig. 368.

Irregular flower. With inequality in the size, form
   or union of its similar parts; not radially sym-
   metrical. Same as zygomorphic. Fig. 369.

Keel. A dorsal projecting usually central rib, like
   the keel of a boat; also the name for the 2
   anterior united petals of a papilionaceous
   "sweetpea" flower as figured on the right-hand
   drawing. Fig. 370.

2 KEELED
FRUIT

IRREGULAR FLOWERS
Fig. 369.

KEELS
KEEL
Fig. 370.

Labiate. Lipped. Belonging to the Labiatae or mint
   family.

Lacerate. Irregularly cut or cleft, as if torn.

Laciniate. Narrowly incised or slashed; margins cut
   in narrow and usually pointed lobes. Fig. 371.

Lacuna (pl. lacunae). An air space in the midst of
   tissue.

Lamella (pl. lamellae). A thin flat plate or laterally flattened ridge. The drawing shows a fruit
   in longitudinal section. Fig. 372.

Lanate. With long tangled woolly hairs. Fig. 373.

-LAMELLA

LACINIATE
LEAF MARGINS
Fig. 371.

LAMELLAE IN FRUIT
Fig. 372.

LANATE SURFACE
Fig. 373.

Lanceolate. Lance-shaped; several
times longer than wide, broadest
toward the base and tapering to
apex. Fig. 374.

LANCEOLATE
LEAF

Fig. 374.

Lateral. Borne on the sides of a structure or object.

Latex. The milky juice of some plants like milkweed
and dandelion.

Lax. Loose; often used for a soft open inflorescence
or for soft drooping stems or foliage.

Leaflet. One of the divisions of a compound leaf.

Legume. The characteristic fruit of
the Leguminosae family; usually
a dehiscent fruit formed from 1
carpel with 2 lines of dehiscence.
Also used for any plant with this
type of fruit. Fig. 375.

LEGUME
FRUIT

Fig. 375.

Lenticel. A group of loose corky cells
formed beneath the epidermis of
woody plants, rupturing the epidermis and admitting gases to and from
the inner tissues. Fig. 376.

LENTICELS
ON TWIG

Fig. 376.

Lenticular. Lens-shaped; biconvex in shape
In the drawing the object is cut into 2
parts. Fig. 377.

LENTICULAR
Fig. 377.

Lepidote. Covered with small scurfy scales like
the leaf of Elaeagnus (Russian Olive).

Ligulate. Furnished with a ligule; also used for a
strap shape like a ligule.

Ligule. The flattened, usually strap-shaped corolla
in the ray flowers of Compositae. Also a hair-
like or membranous projection up from the inside
of a grass sheath at its junction with the blade.
Fig. 378.

Limb. The expanded portion of a gamopetalous corolla
above the throat; the expanded portion of any
organ. Fig. 379.

Linear. Narrow and flat with sides parallel, like a
grass leaf blade. Fig. 380.

LIGULE OF COMPOSITAE

THROAT

TUBE

LIMB OF COROLLA

LINEAR LEAF

Fig. 378.   Fig. 379.   Fig. 380.

Lip. Either the upper or lower division of a bilabiate or 2-lipped corolla. Also the upper (but
by twisting of the pedicel appearing to be the
lower) petal in Orchidaceae.

Lobe. Any segment of an organ especially if rounded.

Lobed. Bearing lobes; loosely
used but technically cut in
not over half way to the base
or midvein, the sinuses and
apex of segments rounded.
The left figure shows a pinnately lobed leaf, the right
a palmately lobed one.
Fig. 381.

LOBED LEAVES
Fig. 381.

Lobulate. With small lobes.

Locule. The cell or compartment of an ovary or anther.

Loculicidal. A dehiscent fruit splitting down the center of a compartment or locule. Fig. 382.

LOCULICIDAL FRUIT

Fig. 382.

Loment. A legume fruit conspicuously constricted between the seeds. Fig. 383.

Lunate. Crescent-shaped like the crescent moon. Fig. 384.

LOMENT FRUIT

Fig. 383.

LUNATE

Fig. 384.

Lyrate. Pinnatifid with the terminal segment large and rounded and the lower lobes small. Fig. 385.

LYRATE LEAF

Fig. 385.

Macrospore. Same as megaspore.

Malpighiaceous. Straight hairs seemingly attached by their middle, pick-shaped. Same as dolabriform, see this for sketches.

Many. Eleven or more. Same as numerous.

Marcescent. Withering but still persistent.

Mealy. A surface covered with minute particles these usually rounded.

Medial. Refers to the middle of a structure.

Megasporangium. (pl. megasporangia). The containing structure for the large spores or megaspores.

Megaspore. The larger of the two kinds of spores, used particularly in the Pteridophytes.

Membranaceous. Same as membranous.

Membranous. Thin, more or less translucent and pliable; loosely used in grasses for any thin structure.

Mericarp. A portion of a fruit that splits away as a seemingly separate unit, most commonly used for the two halves of the fruit of Umbelliferae. Fig. 386.

MERICARP

Fig. 386.

Meristem. Tissue with cells not as yet different-iated, often exhibiting active cell division.

-merous. A suffix indicating division into parts. A "5-merous flower" would have 5 sepals, 5 petals, 5 stamens and a 5 carpellate pistil (providing all these structures were present).

Mesocarp. The middle layer of the pericarp. For an example see figure for drupe.

Mesophyte. A plant that grows under medium or average conditions especially of moisture supply. Compare hydrophyte and xerophyte.

Meter. (Abbreviation M. or m.). Unit of measurement consisting of 100 centimeters; almost 40 inches.

Micron. A microscopic unit of measurement, 1/1000 of a millimeter.

Microsporangium (pl. microsporangia). The containing structure for the small spores or microspores.

Microspore. The smaller kind of spore when 2 types are present; used especially in the Pteridophytes.

Midrib. The main or central rib of a leaf. Fig. 387.

MIDRIB

Fig. 387.

Millimeter. (Abbreviation mm.).
    A small unit of measurement,
    1/10 of a centimeter or
    about 1/25 of an inch.

Monadelphous. Stamens united
    by their filaments into one
    set. Fig. 388.

MONADELPHOUS   MONILIFORM
   STAMENS   FRUIT
Fig. 388. Fig. 389.

Moniliform. Cylindrical with
    rounded contractions at reg-
    ular intervals, resembling a
    string of beads. Fig. 389.

Monoecious. Flowers unisexual but the staminate and
    pistillate ones borne on the same plant.

Monophyllous. Used for leaves in plants where re-
    lated species have compound leaves, but the
    leaflets here reduced to one.

Monotypic. When refering to a genus, then one with
    only a single species in it.

Moss-like. With low thin stems and small thin
    leaves like a moss plant.

Mucilaginous. Slimy or mucilage-like.

Mucro. A short, small, abrupt tooth-like
    tip; loosely used but not very sharp
    at extreme apex. Compare cuspidate.
    Fig. 390.

MUCRO
ON LEAF TIP
Fig. 390.

Mucronate. Tipped with a mucro.

Mucronulate. Minutely mucronate, the mucro very
    small.

Multicellular. Consisting of many cells or small
    compartments.

Multicipital. With many heads, referring to the
    crown of a single root or to several caudices.

Multifid. Cleft into many lobes or segments, these
    usually narrow.

166

Multiple fruit. One formed from several flowers crowded into a single unit on a common axis, as in the mulberry.

Muricate. Roughened with short hard points. Fig. 391.

MURICATE FRUIT
Fig. 391.

Muriculate. Very finely muricate.

Muticous. Blunt and without a point.

Naked. Lacking some structure, appendage or hairs which might ordinarily be expected to be present.

Nectary. A gland or tissue for secreting nectar; often located in highly specialized structures which may themselves be called "nectaries".

Needle-like. Long, slender, rather rigid and more or less sharp at apex like a needle. Usually round or square in cross-section but sometimes flattened. See acerose for drawings.

Nerve. A simple or unbranched vein or slender rib.

Nerviform. On the order of a nerve.

Netted. Same as reticulated.

Net-veined. The veins joining together on the order of a fish net.

Neuter. Without functional stamens or pistils. Same as neutral.

Neutral. See neuter.

Node. The place on a stem where leaves or branches normally originate; the place on an axis that bears other structures; any swollen or knob-like structure. See internode for a figure.

Nodose. Knobby or knotty.

Nodulose. Provided with minute knobs.

Numerous. Eleven or more. Same as many.

167

<u>Nut</u>. A 1-seeded, indehiscent fruit with a hard wall.

Nutlet. A small nut or nut-
   like fruit; used es-
   pecially for the sepa-
   rating lobes of the
   mature ovary in
   Boraginaceae, Labiatae
   and Verbenaceae. The
   drawing shows 2 of the
   4 nutlets. Fig. 392.

SECTION SHOWING
NUTLETS
Fig. 392.

Ob-. A prefix signifying inversion.

Obcompressed. Flattened opposite to the usual way,
   for example flattened dorso-ventrally instead
   of laterally.

Obconical. Inversely cone-shaped, attached at the pointed end. The drawing shows a 3-dimensional figure.
   Fig. 393.

OBCONICAL
Fig. 393.

Obcordate. Inverted heart-shaped, attached at the
   point. Also used in reference to a deeply notch-
   ed apex irrespective of the general leaf shape.
   Fig. 394.

Oblanceolate. Inversely lanceolate, attached at the
   tapered end. Fig. 395.

Oblique. Sides unequal, especially the base of a
   leaf. Fig. 396.

OBCORDATE LEAF
Fig. 394.

OBLANCEOLATE
LEAF
Fig. 395.

OBLIQUE BASE
Fig. 396.

Oblong. Two to four times longer than wide and the
    sides parallel or nearly so. Fig. 397.

Obovate. Inversely ovate, attached at the narrow
    end. Fig. 398.

Obovoid. A 3-dimensional figure of obovate outline.

Obsolete. Rudimentary or not at all evident; par-
    ticularly applied to organs usually present.

Obtuse. Blunt or rounded at the apex. Fig. 399.

BROADLY   NARROWLY
OBLONG LEAVES

Fig. 397.

OBOVATE LEAF

Fig. 398.

OBTUSE TIPS

Fig. 399.

Ochroleucous. Yellowish-white or cream-colored.

Ocrea (pl. ocreae). A tubular stipule or pair of
    sheathing confluent elongated stipules. Char-
    acteristic in the family Polygonaceae. Fig. 400.

Odd-pinnate. A pinnately compound leaf with a
    single terminal leaflet. Fig. 401.

OCREA

Fig. 400.

ODD-PINNATE LEAF

Fig. 401.

169

Oil tube. Small longitudinal ducts in the walls of
the fruit of Umbelliferae presumably containing
volatile oils. Fig. 402.

Oogonium (pl. oogonia). The container for the
oospore.

Oospore. The egg cell with a somewhat hardened outer
coat.

Opposite. Leaves 2 at a node and situated across
the stem from each other. Fig. 403.

Orbicular. A 2-dimensional figure circular in outline. Compare spherical. Fig. 404.

OIL
TUBE

OIL TUBES IN
UMBELLIFERAE FRUIT
Fig. 402.

OPPOSITE LEAVES
Fig. 403.

ORBICULAR LEAF
Fig. 404.

Oval. Loosely used for broadly elliptical, the
width over ½ the length; some authors have used
it as the same as ovate. Fig. 405.

Ovary. That part of the pistil that contains the
ovules. The ovary is shown in longitudinal
section. Fig. 406.

Ovate. Egg-shaped in outline, attached at the wide
end. Fig. 407.

OVAL LEAF
Fig. 405.

STIGMA
STYLE
OVULE   PISTIL
OVARY
OVARY
Fig. 406.

OVATE LEAF
Fig. 407.

Ovoid. A 3-dimensional figure, ovate in outline.

Ovule. The structure that develops into the seed. The ovary is shown in longitudinal section. Fig. 408.

Palate. A rounded projection on the lower lip of a bilabiate corolla, closing the throat. Fig. 409.

OVARY

OVULE

OVULE
Fig. 408.

LOWER LIP   UPPER LIP

PALATE

PALATE ON PERSONATE COROLLA
Fig. 409.

Palea (pl. paleae or paleas). A chaffy scale or bract; the inner of the 2 bracts enclosing the grass flower. Compare lemma.

Paleaceous. Chaffy, thin, small and often translucent.

Palmate. The lobes or divisions attached or running down toward one place at the base. Compare pinnate. Also used to describe the veins of certain leaves. Fig. 410 and Fig. 411.

DIVIDED   PARTED   COMPOUND
PALMATE
Fig. 410.

PALMATELY VEINED
Fig. 411.

Palustrine. Inhabiting wet ground, marsh dwelling.

Pandurate. Fiddle-shaped. Same as panduriform. Fig. 412.

Panduriform. Same as pandurate.

Panicle. A compound inflorescence with the younger flowers at the apex or center; a compound raceme or corymb. The "rachis" may be called the "main axis" by some manuals. Fig. 413.

Paniculate. Borne in a panicle; resembling a panicle.

Pannose. With the texture of felt or closely woven woolen cloth.

Papery. Thin and usually whitish like paper. Compare chartaceous which is usually thick-papery.

Papilionaceous. Like the "sweetpea" type flower of Leguminosae with standard (banner) wings and keel. Fig. 414.

PANDURATE LEAF
Fig. 412.

PRIMARY BRANCH
PEDICEL
RACHIS
FLOWER
PEDUNCLE
PANICLE
Fig. 413.

BANNER
WING
KEEL
PAPILIONACEOUS FLOWER
Fig. 414.

Papilla (pl. papillae). A minute nipple-shaped projection. Fig. 415.

PAPILLAE
Fig. 415.

Papillose. Bearing papillae.

Pappus. The modified calyx limb in Compositae, forming a crown of various character at the summit of the achene. Fig. 416.

PAPPUS TYPES OF COMPOSITAE

NONE SCALES HAIRS CROWN DOUBLE
Fig. 416.

Parallel veined. A leaf with the veins running parallel to each other, usually all about the same size (except sometimes the midrib) and the connections between obscure. Characteristic of the leaf of Monocotyledoneae. Fig. 417.

PARALLEL VEINED LEAVES
Fig. 417.

Parasite. An organism growing upon and obtaining nourishment from another; usually lacking chlorophyll in plants.

Parasitic. Like a parasite.

Parietal. Borne on or pertaining to the wall or inner surface of an ovary or fruit. Drawing number 1 shows only one placenta, number 2 has two placentae showing. Fig. 418.

(2.)   (1.)
PARIETAL PLACENTATION
Fig. 418.

Parted. Lobed or cut in over half-way and usually very near to the base or midrib. The sinuses and segments may be sharp or rounded. Fig. 419.

PINNATELY   PALMATELY
PARTED LEAVES
Fig. 419.

Pectinate. Pinnatifid with the segments narrow and arranged like the teeth of a comb; comb-like. Fig. 420.

PECTINATE LEAF
Fig. 420.

173

Pedicel. The stalk to a single flower of an inflorescence; also used as a stalk to a grass
spikelet. Compare peduncle.

Pedicellate. Borne on a pedicel.

Pedicelled. With a pedicel. Same as pedicellate.

Peduncle. The stalk to a solitary flower or to an
inflorescence. Compare pedicel. Fig. 421.

Pedunculate. Borne upon a peduncle.

Pellucid. Clear and transparent.

Peltate. Shield-shaped, attached to the center or
near the center, at least in-a-ways from the
margin, on the order of an umbrella. Fig. 422.

Pendulous. More or less hanging or declined.

Penta-. Used as a prefix meaning "five".

Pepo. The fleshy indehiscent fruit characteristic
of the Cucurbitaceae. It differs from a berry
chiefly by having a hard, more or less thickened
rind.

Perennial. A plant lasting for 3 or more years; a
stem not dying back over winter.

Perfect. A flower with both functional stamens and
pistils.

Perfoliate. Where the leaf has the stem apparently
passing through it, or where opposite leaves are
joined around the stem at their bases. Fig. 423.

SOLITARY   RACEME
FLOWER
Fig. 421.

PELTATE LEAF
Fig. 422.

PERFOLIATE STEMS
Fig. 423.

174

Perianth. The floral envelope consisting of calyx and corolla however incomplete or modified. Used particularly when the calyx and corolla cannot be readily distinguished.

Pericarp. The wall of the ripened ovary and therefore the wall of the fruit. Sometimes 3 layers can be distinguished, the exocarp (outer), mesocarp (middle) and endocarp (inner). See drupe.

Perigynous. Situated around but not attached to the ovary or its base directly; a flower with stamens and pistils on the calyx tube and the ovary superior. Fig. 424.

PERIGYNOUS FLOWER
Fig. 424.

Persistent. Remaining attached after like parts ordinarily fall off.

Personate. Two-lipped (as a corolla) the throat closed by a prominent palate. See palate for drawing.

Petal. One of the individual parts of the corolla, used particularly for a polypetalous corolla in designating one unit.

Petaloid. Resembling a petal in some way, usually colored other than green.

Petiolate. With a petiole.

Petiole. The stalk to a leaf blade or to a compound leaf. Fig. 425.

Fig. 425.

Petiolule. The stalk to a leaflet in a compound leaf. For drawing see petiole.

Phyllary. A special name sometimes used for an involucral bract on the head of Compositae.

Pilose. With long soft straight hairs. Fig. 426.

PILOSE
Fig. 426.

Pinna (pl. pinnae). One of the first or primary divisions of a pinnately compound or decompound leaf; used especially in ferns. Fig. 427.

Pinnate. Compound leaf with the leaflets on 2 opposite sides of an elongated axis. Fig. 428.

Pinnatifid. Pinnately lobed, cleft or parted usually $\frac{1}{2}$ way in to the midrib or more. Fig. 429.

PINNAE
Fig. 427.

ODD   EVEN
PINNATELY COMPOUND LEAVES
Fig. 428.

PINNATIFID
Fig. 429.

Pinnule. The pinnate segment of a pinna in a bipinnate leaf. In a tripinnate leaf the pinnules are again pinnately divided. See pinna for drawing.

Fig. 430.

Pistil. The seed-producing organ, consisting usually of ovary, style and stigma. The drawing shows a pistil split longitudinally. Fig. 430.

Pistillate. Provided with pistils, used when stamens are lacking.

Pith. The spongy center of a stem, surrounding or joining to the inner part of the vascular bundles. Fig. 431

Fig. 431.

Pitted. Marked with small depressions or pits. Fig. 432.

PITTED

Fig. 432.

Placenta (pl. placentae). Any part of the interior of an ovary that bears ovules. See parietal, axile and free central placentation.

Plane. With flat surface.

Plano-convex. An object usually a fruit or seed, flat on one side and convex on the other. The drawing shows a seed cut in 2 sections. Fig. 433.

PLANO CONVEX SEED

Fig. 433.

Plicate. Folded in plaits, usually lengthwise on the order of a folding fan. Fig. 434.

Plumose. Hairs with side hairs along the main axis like the plume of a feather. Fig. 435.

Plumule. The stem- and leaf-producing structure of an embryo in the seed.

Pod. Any dry dehiscent fruit, often used as a synonym for legume.

Pollen. The male spores in an anther.

Pollinium (pl. pollinia). A mass of waxy or coherent pollen grains as in Asclepias or Orchidaceae. Fig. 436.

PLICATE
Fig. 434.

PLUMOSE STYLE
Fig. 435.

MILKWEED TYPE   ORCHID TYPE
POLLINIA
Fig. 436.

Polygamo-dioecious. Polygamous but chiefly
dioecious; having bisexual flowers and unisexual
flowers on separate individuals.

Polygamo-monoecious. Polygamous but chiefly monoecious; having bisexual flowers and unisexual
flowers on the same individual.

Polygamous. Having bisexual flowers and unisexual
flowers on the same or on different individuals.
This term is not always uniformly used.

Polymorphous. With several forms;
variable as to habit.

Polypetalous. The petals completely separate from each other.

Polysepalous. Calyx with separate
sepals.

POME
LONG SECTION
Fig. 437.

Pome. A fleshy indehiscent fruit with
an inferior ovary and more than one
locule; of the apple type.
Fig. 437.

PORES

Poricidal fruit. A dehiscent fruit,
the seeds escaping through pores.
Fig. 438.

PORICIDAL CAPSULE
Fig. 438.

Posterior. On the side next to or
close to the axis. Compare anterior.

Precocious. Appearing or developing
very early; used in Salix where the
aments develop before the leaves.

Prickle. A small, usually slender outgrowth of the young bark, coming
off with it. Compare spine and
thorn. Fig. 439.

PRICKLES
Fig. 439.

Primocane. The first year's cane (shoot), usually
flowerless in the brambles (Rubus).

178

Procumbent. Lying or trailing on the ground, usually not rooting at the nodes. See prostrate. Fig. 440.

PROCUMBENT STEM

Fig. 440.

Proliferous. Producing bulbs or plantlets from leaves or other offshoots.

Prostrate. Lying flat on the ground, if a stem then may or may not root at nodes. See procumbent for drawing.

Prothallus (pl. **prothallia**). A usually flat thallus-like growth resulting from the germination of a spore, upon which are produced sexual organs or new plants.

Proximad. Toward the point of attachment.

Proximal. The end of an organ by which it is attached.

Pruinose. With a waxy powdery usually whitish covering, this usually rubbing off readily; glaucous to a conspicuous degree.

Pseudo-. A prefix meaning false.

Puberulent. With very short hairs; minutely pubescent. Fig. 441.

PUBERULENT
Fig. 441.

Pubescent. Loosely used for covered with hairs; technically with short soft hairs. Fig. 442.

PUBESCENT
Fig. 442.

Pulvinate. Cushioned or shaped like a close thick mat or cushion.

Punctate. Dotted with depressions, or with transluscent internal glands or colored dots.

Puncticulate. Minutely punctate.

Pungent. Tipped with a sharp rigid point. Fig. 443.

PUNGENT LEAF TEETH
Fig. 443.

179

Pustulose. Beset with pimple-
like elevated areas. Same
as pustulate. Fig. 444.

PUSTULOSE
Fig. 444.

Pyriform. Pear-shaped. Fig. 445.

Pyxis. A capsule with circumscissle dehiscence, the
top coming off as a lid. Fig. 446.

Quill-like. Terete, more or less tapering, usually
hollow. Fig. 447.

PYRIFORM FRUIT
Fig. 445.

PYXIS
Fig. 446.

QUILL-LIKE LEAF
Fig. 447.

Quinate. With five nearly similar
structures (as leaflets) from a common point. Fig. 448.

QUINATE LEAFLETS
Fig. 448.

Raceme. An inflorescence with pedicelled
flowers borne along a more or less
elongated axis with the younger flowers
nearest the apex. Fig. 449.

FLOWER
BRACT
RACHIS

PEDUNCLE

RACEME
Fig. 449.

Racemiform. In the form of a raceme.

Racemose. Raceme-like or bearing racemes.

Rachilla. A small rachis; applied particularly to the axis of a grass spikelet, and to the secondary axis in sedges.

Rachis. The central elongated axis to an inflorescence or a compound leaf. See raceme for example.

Radiate. Spreading from or arranged around a common center. In Compositae meaning with ray-flowers.

Radical. Belonging to the root, or apparently arising from or very near the root. The leaves of dandelion are called radical. Compare rosette. Fig. 450.

Fig. 450.

Rank. A vertical row; for example leaves that are 2-ranked are in 2 rows along the stem.

Ray. The branch of an umbel or a similar inflorescence. The ligulate or strap-shaped flower in the Compositae, used especially for marginal flowers different from the central regular ones. Fig. 451.

UMBELLIFERAE
Fig. 451 1st

COMPOSITAE
Fig. 451 2nd

Receptacle. The more or less expanded portion of the flower stalk that bears the organs of a flower or the collected flowers of a head as in Compositae.

Reclinate. Turned or bent abruptly downward.

Reclining. Lying upon something.

Recumbent. Leaning or reposing upon the ground.

Recurved. Curved outward, downward or backward.

181

Reflexed. Abruptly bent or turned downward or back-ward.

Regular. A flower with all the members of each set alike in form, size and color; radially sym-metrical.

Reniform. Kidney-shaped, usually attached at the center of the incurved side. Fig. 452.

Repand. With a wavy surface or margin, not as deep as sinuate. Same as undulate.

Replum. The septum of certain dry dehiscent fruits, persisting after the valves have fallen away; used in the Cruciferae. Fig. 453.

Reticulate. In the form of a network; leaf veins in a network. Fig. 454.

RENIFORM LEAF
Fig. 452.

REPLUM

Fig. 453.

RETICULATE SURFACE
Fig. 454.

Retrorse. Directed backward or downward.

Retuse. A rounded apex with a shallow notch. Fig. 455.

RETUSE APEX
Fig. 455.

Revolute. Rolled backward from each margin upon the lower side. Op-posite of involute. Fig. 456.

REVOLUTE LEAF
Fig. 456.

Rhizoid. Root-like but of simple structure.

182

Rhizomatous. Having the characters of a rhizome. Sometimes written rhizomatose.

Rhizome. Any prostrate more or less elongated stem growing partly or completely beneath the surface of the ground; usually rooting at the nodes and becoming upcurved at apex. See rootstock. Fig. 457.

RHIZOME
GROUND LINE

Fig. 457.

Rhombic. Outline of an equilateral oblique-angled figure; 4-sided like a diamond shape. Fig. 458.

RHOMBIC LEAF
Fig. 458.

Rhomboid. A solid figure rhombic in outline.

Rib. A primary or prominent vein usually of a leaf.

Root. The descending axis of the plant, without nodes and internodes and absorbing moisture from the ground. Roots may appear, however, in unusual places (see adventitious).

Rootlet. A small root; often used for the aerial supporting roots put out by some vines.

Rootstock. A root-like stem or branch under or sometimes on the ground. Like rhizome but loosely used by some to include any elongated underground structure that spreads the plant.

SCAPE

ROSETTE OF LEAVES
Fig. 459.

Rosette. A dense basal cluster of leaves arranged in circular fashion like the leaves of the common dandelion. Fig. 459.

Rostrate. Having a beak. Fig. 460.

BEAKED FRUIT   BEAK OF KEEL
(OXYTROPIS)
ROSTRATE
Fig. 460.

Rosulate. In the form of a rosette.

Rotate. A wheel-shaped corolla with short tube and wide horizontally flaring limb. Fig. 461.

Rudiment. An imperfectly developed, usually minute organ.

Rufous. Reddish-brown.

Rugose. With wrinkled or creased surface. Fig. 462.

Rugulose. Minutely rugose.

Runcinate. Sharply incised or pinnatifid with the segments directed backward. Fig. 463.

ROTATE COROLLA
Fig. 461.

RUGOSE SURFACE
Fig. 462.

RUNCINATE LEAF
Fig. 463.

Runner. A very slender or filiform stolon-like stem rooting at the apex. Fig. 464.

RUNNER

Fig. 464.

Rush-like. Grass-like in general appearance, the flowers usually not colored or conspicuous.

Saccate. Sac-shaped or pouch-shaped.

Sagittate. Shaped like an arrowhead with the basal lobes directed backward. Compare hastate. Fig. 465.

SAGITTATE LEAF
Fig. 465.

Salverform. A corolla with a long slender tube, abruptly flaring into a circular limb. Fig. 466.

Samara. A dry indehiscent winged fruit. Fig. 467.

SALVERFORM
COROLLA
Fig. 466.

SINGLE   DOUBLE
SAMARA
Fig. 467.

Saprophyte. A plant that lives on dead organic material, usually lacking green chlorophyll. Compare parasite.

Scaberulent. Slightly scabrous.

Scaberulous. Slightly scabrous.

Scabrous. Rough or harsh to the touch usually from very short stiff hairs or short sharp projections. The test is to draw the finger tip lightly over the surface. The drawing shows a surface scabrous from short sharp projections. Fig. 468.

SCABROUS
Fig. 468.

Scale. Any thin scarious body resembling the scale of a fish or reptile; often used for such structures present on the basal or underground portion of the plant. Compare bract.

Scape. A naked flowering stem rising from the ground without proper leaves. For a drawing see "radical".

Scapose. Bearing a scape or resembling one.

Scarious. Thin, dry, membranous and more or less transluscent, not green.

185

Schizocarp. A dry fruit of 2 or more carpels,
    splitting up at maturity into 2 or more one-
    seeded, indehiscent segments. Some manuals call
    this fruit a cremocarp at least in part.
    Fig. 469.

Scorpioid. Coiled at the apex like the tail of a
    scorpion, used especially for inflorescences.
    Fig. 470.

SCHIZOCARPS

UMBELLIFERAE   MALVACEAE
        Fig. 469.

SCORPIOID
INFLORESCENCE
        Fig. 470.

Scurfy. Covered with small scale-like or bran-like
    particles.

Secund. Borne or directed to 1 side of the axis.
    Fig. 471.

Seed. The matured ovule, consisting of embryo and
    its coats, with a supply of food.

Sepal. One of the parts of the outer whorl of the
    floral envelope or calyx, usually green in color.

Sepaloid. Of the color or texture of a sepal, or
    resembling one in some way.

Septate. Divided by one or more partitions. Il-
    lustrated for a twig but can be in other
    structures. Fig. 472.

SECUND
FLOWERS
    Fig. 471.

SEPTATE PITH OF TWIG
    Fig. 472.

186

Septicidal. A capsule splitting down
the septa and not through the
locule. Compare loculicidal.
Fig. 473.

SEPTICIDAL CAPSULE
Fig. 473.

Septum. Any kind of a partition.

Sericeous. Covered with long, straight, soft, appressed hairs giving a silky texture. The hairs
are usually more numerous than in the drawing.
Fig. 474.

Serrate. With sharp teeth directed forward. Fig.
475.

SERICEOUS
Fig. 474.

SERRATE   SERRULATE
Fig. 475.

Serrulate. Serrate with small teeth. See serrate
for drawing.

Sessile. Without a stalk of
any kind. Fig. 476.

Seta (pl. setae). A bristle-
like hair.

FLOWER

LEAF

SESSILE
Fig. 476.

Setaceous. Bristle-like.

Setiform. Like or on the order of
a bristle.

Setose. Beset with bristles.
Fig. 477.

SETOSE SURFACE
Fig. 477.

Sheath. A tubular envelope, usually
used for that part of the leaf
of a sedge or grass that en-
velopes the stem.

SIGMOID PEDICEL

Shrub. A woody perennial plant smaller than a tree and usually with
several basal stems. Compare
tree with its drawings.

Fig. 478.

Sigmoid. Doubly-curved like the letter S. Fig.
478.

Silicle. A short fruit of the
family Cruciferae (mustards)
usually not more than twice
as long as wide. Fig. 479.

SILICLE

Fig. 479.

Silique. A fruit of the
mustard family (Cruciferae),
dry, dehiscent and 2-celled,
the septum (replum) thin
with the 2 halves of the
fruit pulling away from it.
Often used to designate a
mustard fruit that is
elongated and longer than
a silicle. Fig. 480.

SILIQUE

Fig. 480.

Silky. Of silk-like appearance caused by long,
straight, soft, appressed hairs. See sericeous.

Simple. Of only 1 part, not completely
divided into separate segments.
Compare compound. Fig. 481.

SIMPLE LEAF

Fig. 481.

Sinuate. Strongly wavy-margined, deeper than undulate or repand. Fig. 482.

SINUATE MARGIN
Fig. 482.

Sinus. The depression or recess between 2 adjoining lobes. Fig. 483.

Smooth. Surface not rough, sometimes loosely used for absence of any hair.

Sordid. Dirty in tint.

Sorus (pl. sori). A cluster of sporangia on a fern frond. The figures show types of indusia. Fig. 484.

LOBE
SINUS
SINUS
Fig. 483.

MARGIN OF FROND
PELTATE
LATERAL
INFERIOR
SORI OF FERN
Fig. 484.

Spadix. A spike with a thick and fleshy axis, usually densely flowered with imperfect flowers. In the figure the lower part of the spathe is cut away to show the lower flowers of the spadix. Fig. 485.

Spathe. A large bract sheathing or enclosing an inflorescence.

Spatulate. Broad and rounded at apex and tapering at base, like a druggist's spatula; flattened spoon-shaped. Fig. 486.

SPATHE
STAMINATE FLOWERS
SPADIX
PISTILLATE FLOWERS
Fig. 485.

SPATULATE LEAF
Fig. 486.

Spherical. A 3-dimensional solid, round in outline, like the earth. Same as globose.

Spicate. Arranged in or resembling a spike.

Spike. An inflorescence with the flowers sessile on a more or less elongated axis with the younger flowers at the apex. Fig. 487.

FLOWER

RACHIS

SPIKE

Fig. 487

Spike-like. Resembling a spike, used where the flowers are on short pedicels or on very short panicle branches.

Spindle-shaped. Broadest at about the middle and tapering both ways. See fusiform for drawing.

Spine. A sharp-pointed rigid deep-seated outgrowth from the stem, not pulling off with the bark. Compare prickle. Sometimes differentiated from thorn by absence of vascular tissue. Fig. 488.

SPINE

Fig. 488.

Spinescent. Bearing a spine or ending in a spine-like sharp point.

Spinulose. Minutely spiny; beset with small spines.

ANNULUS

Sporangium (pl. sporangia). The spore-bearing case in Pteridophytes. Fig. 489.

SPORANGIUM
FERN
Fig. 489.

Spore. The small reproductive body in Pteridophytes.

Sporocarp. The fruit-cases of certain Pteridophytes containing sporangia or spores.

Sporophyll. A spore-bearing leaf, often highly modified.

Sporophyte. The spore-bearing, asexual generation. Used especially in Pteridophytes for the conspicuous plant body. Compare gametophyte.

CORALLA SPURRED   SEPAL SPURRED
Fig. 490.

Sprawling. Lying on or leaning upon or over another object.

Spreading. Diverging nearly at right angles; nearly prostrate.

Spur. A hollow, sac-like or tubular extension of a floral organ, usually nectariferous. Fig. 490.

Squamella (pl. squamellae). A small chaffy bract or scale-like appendage.

Squarrose. Having the parts or processes (usually the tips) spreading or recurved. The drawing shows squarrose bracts of a composite head, the flowers shed. Fig. 491.

SQUARROSE
BRACTS
Fig. 491.

Stamen. One of the pollen-bearing organs of a flower. Made up of filament and anther. Fig. 492.

Staminal tube. The united part of the filaments when this occurs. Fig. 493.

Staminate. Bearing stamens only.

Staminodium (pl. staminodia). A sterile stamen or any structure lacking an anther but corresponding to a stamen. Also written "staminode". Fig. 494.

ANTHER

FILAMENT

STAMEN
Fig. 492.

TUBE   ANTHERS

STAMINAL TUBE
Fig. 493.

STAMINODIUM

STAMEN

Fig. 494.

191

Standard. Same as banner.

Stellate. Star-like or star-shaped
with slender segments or hairs
radiating out from a common
center. Fig. 495.

STELLATE HAIRS
Fig. 495.

Sterile. Infertile and unproductive, as a flower
without a pistil, a stamen without an anther or
a leafy shoot without flowers.

Stigma. That part of the pistil
that receives the pollen, usually at or near the apex of
the pistil and mostly hairy,
papillose or sticky. See
ovary for drawing.

Stigmatic. Belonging to or having the characteristics of a
stigma.

Stipe. The stalk-like support
of a pistil (above the other
flower parts). Also the
name for the petiole of a fern frond. Fig. 496.

Fig. 496. Fig. 496.
1st   2nd

Stipel. An appendage like a stipule but subtending
the leaflet. See stipule for drawing.

Stipitate. Provided with a stipe
or with a slender stalk-like
base.

Stipulate. Provided with stipules.

Stipule. An appendage at the base
of the petiole or leaf at each
side of its insertion; often
more or less united. Fig. 497.

Fig. 497.

Stolon. A trailing shoot above
ground rooting at the nodes.
Compare runner. Fig. 498.

Fig. 498.

Stoloniferous. Bearing stolons.

Stoloniform. On the general order of a stolon.

Stomate (pl. stomata). A small opening on the surface of a leaf through which gaseous exchange takes place. Sometimes written **stoma.**

STRICT

Stramineous. Straw-colored.

Striate. Marked with fine longitudinal lines, grooves, furrows or streaks.

Strict. Very straight and upright. Fig. 499.

Fig. 499.

Strigillose. Like strigose but hairs very short.

Strigose. With appressed, stiff, rather short hairs. Fig. 500.

STRIGOSE
Fig. 500.

Strobilus (pl. strobili). An inflorescence characterized by imbricated bracts or scales as a pine cone. See **cone** for drawing.

Strophiole. An appendage at the hilum of some seeds.

Style. The usually stalk-like part of a pistil connecting the ovary and stigma. See **ovary** for drawing.

Stylopodium. A disk-like expansion of the base of the style as in Umbelliferae. See **schizocarp** for drawing.

Sub-. A prefix meaning almost or below

Subtending. Situated closely beneath something, often enclosing or embracing it.

Subulate. Awl-shaped; narrowly triangular and tapering to a sharp point. Fig. 501.

SUBULATE LEAF
Fig. 501.

Succulent. Fleshy and full of juice.

Suffruticose. Low-shrubby; applied to perennials, the lower part of the stems woody but the upper part herbaceous. Also written **suffrutescent**.

SULCATE STEM
Fig. 502.

Sulcate. Grooved or furrowed, especially if the groove is deep and longitudinal. Fig. 502.

Sulcus. (pl. **sulci**). A furrow or groove.

Superior ovary. An ovary with the perianth inserted below it. Fig. 503.

SUPERIOR OVARY
Fig. 503.

Surculose-proliferous. Producing runners or offsets from the base or from rootstocks.

Suture. A junction or seam of union; a line of dehiscence. Fig. 504.

SUTURE OF A FOLLICLE
Fig. 504.

Sympetalous. Petals more or less united. Same as **gamopetalous**.

Synsepalous. The sepals more or less united. Same as **gamosepalous**.

Taproot. The primary root continuing the axis of the plant downward. Such roots may be thick as in the drawing or comparatively thin. Fig. 505.

TAP ROOT

Fig. 505.

194

Tawny. Dull yellowish with a tinge of brown.

Taxon (pl. taxa). A general term for any morpho-logical unit or group.

Tendril. A slender cauline or foliar outgrowth. Commonly coiling at apex and serving as an organ of support. Fig. 506.

TIP OF STEM   END OF RACHIS   PETIOLE   MODIFIED LEAF

TENDRILS

Fig. 506.

Terete. Circular in cross-section and more or less elongated. Like cylindrical but may be slightly tapering. Fig. 507.

TERETE STEM
Fig. 507.

Ternate. Arranged in three's.

Terrestrial. A plant growing in the air with its basal parts in soil. Compare aquatic with parts immersed in water.

Tessellate. Checkered.

Tetra-angular. With 4 angles.

Thalloid. Resembling or on the order of a thallus.

Thallus. A vegetative often flattened body not differentiated into stems and leaves.

Thorn. A stiff, hard, sharp-pointed emergence more deeply seated than a prickle. By some, differentiated from a spine in having vascular tissue. Fig. 508.

THORN

Fig. 508.

195

Throat. The orifice of a gemopetalous corolla or calyx, at or just below the junction of the tube with the limb. Fig. 509.

Fig. 509.

Thyrse. A contracted, cylindrical or ovoid-pyramidal, usually densely flowered panicle, like a cluster of grapes. Also written thrysus. Fig. 510.

THYRSE
Fig. 510.

Thyrsoid. Resembling a thyrse.

Tomentose. With a dense wool-like covering of matted, intertangled hairs of medium length. Compare lanate and canescent. Fig. 511.

TOMENTOSE
Fig. 511.

Tomentulose. Sparingly or minutely tomentose.

Tomentum. The covering of closely interwoven and tangled hairs in a tomentose surface.

TOROSE FRUIT
Fig. 512.

Torose. Cylindrical in shape with swellings and contractions at intervals. Fig. 512.

To tuous. Twisted or bent.

Torulose. Minutely torose as in a small pod constricted between seeds.

Torus. Same as receptacle.

Trailing. Prostrate but not rooting.

196

Translucent. Transmitting rays of light without be-
    ing transparent.

Tree. A perennial woody plant of considerable
    stature at maturity and with 1 or few main
    trunks. Rather loosely used but a fairly well
    understood concept. Fig. 513.

Trichome. A hair-like outgrowth of the epidermis.

Trifoliate. A compound leaf with 3 leaflets.
    Fig. 514.

TREE   SHRUB
Fig. 513.

PINNATELY   PALMATELY
    TRIFOLIATE
Fig. 514.

Trigonal. Three-angled. Fig. 515.

TRIGONAL STEM
Fig. 515.

Trigonous. Three-angled. Same
    as trigonal.

Tripinnate. Pinnately compound
    3 times; the pinnules again
    pinnate. Fig. 516.

TRIPINNATE LEAF
Fig. 516.

197

Triquetrous. With 3 salient angles,
the sides concave or chanelled.
Fig. 517.

TRIQUETROUS
Fig. 517.

Triternate. Three times ternate;
ternate with the 3 main divisions
once and once-again ternate.
Fig. 518.

TRITERNATE LEAF
Fig. 518.

Truncate. Squared at the tip or
base as if cut off with a
straight blade. Fig. 519.

APEX   BASE
TRUNCATE LEAF
Fig. 519.

Tube. Any hollow cylindrical structure, especially
the tubular basal part of a gamopetalous corolla.

Tuber. A thickened, short usually
subterranean stem having numerous
buds called eyes; like a potato.
Fig. 520.

TUBER
Fig. 520.

Tubercle. A small rounded structure,
often pimple-like. Fig. 521.

TUBERCLES

Fig. 521.

Tuberculate. Bearing small processes or tubercles.

Tufted. Having a cluster of hairs or other slender outgrowths; stems in a very close cluster.

Tumid. Swollen. Fig. 522.

TUMID STEM
Fig. 522.

Tunicated. Having concentric coats as an onion bulb. See bulb for drawing.

Turbinate. Top-shaped; inversely conical. About the same as obconical which see for drawing.

Turgid. Swollen or tightly drawn; said of a thin covering expanded by internal pressure.

Turion. A scaly often succulent shoot produced from a bud on an underground rootstock.

Twining. Ascending by coiling around a support.

Type. In taxonomy the specimens from which the original description was made. (Type specimens.)

Umbel. A convex or flat-topped inflorescence, the flowers all arising from 1 point, the younger in the center. Fig. 523.

Umbellate. In or like an umbel.

Umbellet. A small or secondary umbel in a compound umbel. See umbel for drawing.

Umbonate. Bearing a stout projection in the center; bossed. Fig. 524.

Uncinate. Hooked near the apex or in the form of a hook. Fig. 525.

SIMPLE   COMPOUND
UMBEL
Fig. 523.

UMBONATE
Fig. 524.

UNCINATE BRISTLES
Fig. 525.

Undershrub. A small shrub or a
perennial plant woody only at
the base.

Undulate. The margin gently wavy.
Same as repand. Compare
sinuate. Fig. 526.

UNDULATE MARGIN

Fig. 526.

Unifoliate. A theoretically compound leaf with all
but 1 leaflet suppressed; a simple-appearing
leaf in a group with compound leaves.

Unilateral. Arranged on one side.

Uniseriate. Arranged in one row or series.

Unisexual. With either stamens or pistils, not both.
Compare bisexual and perfect.

Urceolate. Hollow and cylindrical or ovoid
but contracted at or near the mouth
like an urn. Fig. 527.

URCEOLATE
COROLLA

Urn-shaped. Same as urceolate.

Fig. 527.

Utricle. A small thin-walled 1-seeded fruit; any
bladder-like body.

Vaginate. Provided with or surrounded by a sheath.

Valvate. Opening by valves or
provided with valves; also
for parts meeting together
edge to edge without overlapping. Compare imbricate.
Fig. 528.

X SECT.

VALVATE SEPALS IN BUD

Fig. 528.

Valve. One of the parts or segments into which a
dehiscent fruit splits.

Vascular bundle. An elongated group of cells specialized for conduction and often support. In a leaf, the veins.

Vein. Threads of vascular tissue in a leaf or other organ especially those which branch. Compare nerve.

Velum. The fold on the inner side of the leaf base of Isoetes functioning as an indusium.

Ventral. Belonging to the inner or axis side of an organ; the upper surface of a leaf.

Ventricose. Inflated or swollen unequally as on one side. In the drawing the corolla tube is ventricose at its base. Fig. 529.

VENTRICOSE
COROLLA
Fig. 529.

Vernation. The particular arrangement of a leaf or its parts in the bud.

Verrucose. Covered with wart-like elevations. Fig. 530.

VERRUCOSE
Fig. 530.

Versatile. An anther attached at or near its middle and turning freely on its support. Compare basifixed. Fig. 531.

VERSATILE
ANTHER
Fig. 531

Verticil. A circle of 3 or more structures around a common axis.

Verticillate. With 3 or more leaves or other structures arranged in a circle about a stem or other common axis. Same as whorled. In the drawing the leaves are very narrow. Fig. 532.

VERTICILLATE LEAVES
Fig. 532.

Villous. With long, soft, somewhat wavy hairs. Compare pilose. Fig. 533.

VILLOUS
Fig. 533.

Vine. A plant climbing or scrambling on some support, the stem not standing upright of itself.

Virgate. Wand-like, as a slender straight erect stem.

Viscid. Glutinous, sticky or gummy to the touch.

Weed. A troublesome or aggressive plant that intrudes where not wanted. especially a plant that vigorously colonizes disturbed areas. To the rangeman a weed is a herbaceous nongrass-like plant on the range.

Whorled. With 3 or more leaves or other structures arranged in a circle around a stem or some common axis. Same as verticillate which see for sketch.

Wing. Any membranous or thin expansion bordering or surrounding an organ. Also one of the lateral petals in a papilionaceous corolla. See banner for sketch.

Winged. Provided with wings.

Winter annual. A plant where the seed germinates in the fall, the seedling surviving the winter and completing its growth in the spring of the next season.

Woolly. With long, soft interwoven hair. Same as lanate which see for drawing.

Xerophyte. A plant adapted to dry or arid habitats Compare mesophyte and hydrophyte.

Zygomorphic. With inequality in the size, form or union of its similar parts; not radially symmetrical. See irregular flower for sketches.